The Story of
Thomas A. Edison

by Frances M. Perry
with Afterword by Sonya Shafer

The Story of Thomas A. Edison
Originally published in *Four American Inventors* by the American Book
Company, 1901
This edition with additional content from Rutgers University © 2012 by
Simply Charlotte Mason

Cover Design: John Shafer

ISBN 978-1-61634-159-6

Published and printed by
Simply Charlotte Mason, LLC
PO Box 892
Grayson, Georgia 30017
United States

SimplyCharlotteMason.com

Contents

Chapter 1

Early Years

Often in America the children of humble parents have become distinguished men. Some have gained respect by their wise management of public affairs; some are honored because they led our armies to victory; and some are admired by reason of the beautiful stories and poems which they have written. A few men have earned the gratitude of the people by adding to the comfort and happiness of everyday life through their wonderful inventions. Of these last, Thomas Alva Edison is one of the best known examples.

This great inventor may well be called a "self-made" man. His parents were humble people with only a few acquaintances and friends. The father was a hardy laboring man, who came from a family that worked hard and lived long. Mr. Edison made shingles with which to roof houses. He made good shingles, too. At that time this work was not done by machinery, but by hand. Mr. Edison employed several workmen to help him. He was industrious and thrifty.

When Thomas Edison was born, on the eleventh of February, eighteen forty-seven, the shingle-maker lived in Milan, a village in Erie county, Ohio. His home was a

Birthplace of Thomas A. Edison

modest brick cottage on Choate avenue. The house was built on a bluff overlooking the valley where the Huron river flows, with the canal beside it.

In harvest time the little village was a busy place. All day huge farm wagons drawn by four or six horses rumbled along the dusty roads, carrying grain to the canal. For the farmers from far and near brought their grain to Milan to send it by canal to Lake Erie. Often as many as six hundred wagon loads of grain came to the village in a single day. The narrow canal was crowded with barges and sailing vessels which were being loaded with it.

Little Thomas Edison was not content to watch this busy scene from his home on the hill. At a very early age he went with the older boys to have a closer view. He soon learned to go about the village, and, when he was no older than many children who are never allowed outside of the nurse's sight, he trotted about along and felt very much at his ease among the farmers and rough workmen.

Thomas was a serious looking child. He had a large head covered with a wayward shock of hair, which would not curl nor even part straight. He had a broad, smooth forehead, which was drawn into wrinkles when anything puzzled him. His big eyes looked out from beneath heavy brows, with wonder in childhood, with keenness when he grew older. Whenever his brow scowled, his thin lips were pressed tightly together. Even when the child smiled his chin looked very square and firm. The strangers who noticed him said, not, "What a pretty child," but, "What a smart-looking boy!"

The father believed that the best thing he could do for his son was to train him to be industrious. The mother had been a school teacher. She considered an education an important part of a boy's preparation for life. Both parents began early to do what seemed to them their duty towards their son. His father required him to use his hands. His mother taught him to use his head.

He was an eager pupil. An old man in Milan remembers seeing Edison, when he was a youngster in dresses, sitting upon the ground in front of a store, trying to copy the store sign on a board with a piece of chalk. He went to school very little. He could learn much faster at home, where he did not have to go through the formality of raising his hand every time he wanted to ask a question; he wanted to ask a great many.

When Edison was still a mere child, a railroad was built through Milan. Then the farmers used the railroad instead of the canal for shipping their grain. For that reason there was less business in Milan than before the road was built. Many families that had done work in connection with the canal moved away. The place became so dull that Mr. Edison found it hard to make a living there. Accordingly, when Thomas was seven years old, Mr. Edison moved his family to Port Huron, Michigan.

Mr. Edison once said that his son had had no childhood. We have seen that as a child he was a little "sobersides," too busy getting acquainted with the world around him to care for play. As he grew older, his face lost its solemn look. He became an active fun-loving boy. But he differed from other boys in that he found his "fun" in doing things which most boys would have called work.

Chapter 2

Youthful Business Ventures

W hen Thomas, or Alva (he was called by his middle name during his boyhood) was twelve years of age, his father considered him old enough to earn his own living. He was therefore willing to have him take a position as train boy on the Grand Trunk Railroad.

Young Edison was just the person to enjoy a train boy's life. He was fitted to make a success of the business. Forward and self-confident, he had a pleasant, jovial manner which made him popular with strangers. He was quick-witted enough to say just the thing about his wares to amuse or interest the passengers. And he sold enough newspapers and sweetmeats to clear a good profit.

Besides, he was shrewd and self-reliant. Finding that the sale of papers depended on the news they contained, he looked them over carefully before buying, and soon learned to judge accurately the number he could sell.

The Civil War was then going on, and when there was exciting war news, papers were in great demand. One day he opened the paper and found an account of the battle of Pittsburg Landing. He said to himself, "I could sell a thousand of these papers, if I had them, and if the people at the stations only knew there had been a battle." Here were two big "ifs," but the boy promptly made up his mind how to overcome them.

He went to the telegraph office and sent dispatches to the towns at which his train stopped, announcing that a terrible battle had been fought. He felt sure that the news would spread rapidly through the villages, and crowds would be at the stations waiting for the papers.

He then went to the newspaper office and asked the business manager to sell him one thousand copies of the *Detroit Free Press*, on credit. The manger refused curtly. Nothing daunted the boy sought the office of the editor, Mr. W. F. Story. "I am the newsboy on the Grand Trunk Railroad, from Detroit to Port Huron, and I should like to have one thousand copies of today's *Press*, containing the account of the battle," he said blandly. "I have no money to pay for them, but I am sure I shall be able to pay you out of the proceeds of the day's sale."

The editor looked at him in surprise. "And where do you expect to find purchasers for so many papers?" he asked. When he heard what the youth had done to secure his customers, he smiled and gave him an order for the papers.

Edison was not mistaken; he found his papers in such demand that he was able to raise the price first to ten cents, then to twenty-five cents. He made what seemed to him a fortune out of the day's work.

Profit in money was not, however, all that Thomas Edison gained from his experience as train boy. The busy, varied life he led was in many ways an education to the active, wide-awake boy. While attending to his work he gave it his undivided attention. But when he had finished it, he dismissed it from his mind and interested himself in other things.

He learned a good deal about the country through which he traveled every day. Most boys are thoroughly well acquainted with the one town in which they live, but he knew Detroit as well as Port Huron, and was familiar with the geography and business of the country and villages between those cities.

His train was a mixed train, made up of freight and passenger cars. The newsboy considered himself a very important part of that train. He knew it from engine to caboose, and was on good terms with all the trainmen. Indeed, he felt an interest and pride not only in "my train," but in "my road," as he called the Grand Trunk Railroad. He knew its officers, its trainmen, its station agents, the telegraph operators, and even the trackmen. He could always be depended upon for the latest railroad news either in the nature of business or personal gossip.

Finding that others were as much interested as he in what was going on along the road, but were slower in finding it out, he decided to print a railroad newspaper. He got some old type from the office of the *Detroit Free Press* where he had made friends, and set up a printing office in the corner of a freight car. One half of the car was fitted up as a smoker, and the newsboy took possession of the unused half. There, when he had nothing else to do, he worked hard on a paper of which he was proprietor, editor, business manager, reporter, and printer.

He issued his paper weekly and called it *The Grand Trunk Herald*. It was a small paper consisting of two sheets printed on one side only. It was poorly printed, and the grammar and punctuation were often faulty, but it contained much that was of interest to those who were connected with the railroad. Besides such business items as changes in time, the connections made with the train by stage coaches, and announcements of articles lost and found, it was filled with current railroad news and observations by the editor, which give us a good idea of the character and habits of the boy. Here are some extracts from the *Herald*:

"Heavy shipments at Baltimore; we were delayed the other day at New Baltimore Station, waiting for a friend, and while waiting took upon ourselves to have a peep at things generally; we saw in the freight house of the G. T. R. 400 barrels of flour and 150 hogs waiting for shipment to Portland."

"John Robinson, baggage master at James Creek Station, fell off the platform yesterday and hurt his leg. The boys are sorry for John."

"No. 3 Burlington engine has gone into the shed for repairs."

"The more to do the more done. We have observed along the line of railway at the different stations where there is only one Porter, such as at Utica, where he is fully engaged from morning until late at night, that he has everything clean and in first-class order, even on the platforms the snow does not lie for a week after it has fallen, but is swept off before it is almost down, at other stations, where there is two Porters, things are *vice-versa*."

"Premiums. We believe that the Grand Trunk Railway give premiums every six months to their engineers who use the least wood and oil running the usual journey. Now we have rode with Mr. E. L. Northrop, one of their engineers, and we do not believe you could fall in with another engineer more careful or attentive to his engine, being the most steady driver that we have ever rode behind (and we consider ourselves some judge having been railway riding for over two years constantly) always kind and obliging and ever at his post. His engine we contend does not cost one fourth for repairs what the other engines do. We would respectfully recommend him to the kindest consideration of the G. T. R. officers."

The good-natured self-importance of the young editor, with his pompous editorial "We," is amusing. But though the reader may smile at the fourteen-year-old boy's recommendation of the experienced engineer to the attention of the railroad officer, he feels that the writer must have been a sensible boy and that he knew what he was talking about. Edison's remarks about the well-kept station house show the boy's appreciation of order and punctual attention to duty. What he has to say is sensible and sincere, and it is not surprising that he found readers.

He had over three hundred subscribers for his paper, at three cents a copy. Of course the readers of the *Herald* were all railroad men.

This little sheet gained some notoriety, however, and was mentioned in a London paper as the only newspaper in the world published on a train.

Edison's success with the *Herald* induced him to undertake to print a paper of more general interest. His second paper was called *Paul Pry*. In this paper Edison used great freedom in expressing opinions of men and things. On one occasion a personal paragraph in his paper so angered a reader, that, seeing the editor near the river, he gave him a good ducking. This severe punishment dampened the youthful editor's enthusiasm for journalism, and he gave up the business a short time after the occurrence.

Chapter 3

Study

A boy who writes his ideas for others to read is pretty sure to be interested in reading what others have written. This was the case with Edison. He realized that there was a good deal in books that was worth knowing. He had no one to guide him in selecting his reading, but that did not trouble him. Life seemed long, and books were very little things. There was surely time enough for an industrious person to read them all. He determined to begin with the Free Library of Detroit.

He picked out a shelf of particularly large, wise-looking books and commenced reading. Among these books were: Gibbon's *Decline and Fall of the Roman Empire*, Hume's *History of England*, Burton's *Anatomy of Melancholy*, and Newton's *Principia*.

A large part of the contents of these books was too advanced for the understanding of the young reader. Nevertheless he kept cheerfully at the task he had set for himself, until he had finished all the books on a shelf fifteen feet long.

He had learned a great many interesting facts from this difficult reading. But perhaps the most valuable lessons the experience taught him were about books. He had discovered for himself that it was both impossible and undesirable to read all books; that some had in them very little that was of value to him, and were not worth the time it took to read them, while others deserved the closest study. In fact he had become something of a critic, and was able to judge for himself whether a book would interest and help him. He did not stop reading when he had finished the shelf, but henceforth he chose his books with more care.

Some of the books that he read troubled him, because he could not wholly understand them, and he was always on the lookout for some one who knew enough to explain the difficulties to him. Other books filled his mind with new ideas and made him think very hard. An old chemistry excited him so much that he could think of nothing but the wonderful statements it contained about even such simple things as air, water, fire. He was curious to experiment with some of the strange elements mentioned in it, such as oxygen, nitrogen, and hydrogen. Thomas Edison was not the boy to sit still and wonder when his curiosity was aroused. He thought it would be a fine thing to have a workroom or laboratory, all fitted out with materials and implements for making chemical experiments, and he determined to have one.

His first step towards the realization of this ambition was to get acquainted with a chemist. The next, was to buy such second-hand apparatus as he could with the money he had saved, and get a few of the cheaper chemicals. These he arranged neatly in the corner of the freight car which was his newspaper office. The little bottles with their glass stopples and mysterious contents were exceedingly precious to him, and lest some one should meddle with them, he pasted poison labels on all of them.

In his rude little laboratory the inventor made his first experiments. He found this a very fascinating pastime. He was willing to work hard, dress poorly, and eat plain food for the sake of his laboratory. Without a teacher, with only a book to instruct him, he experimented until he had learned the properties and powers of many chemical substances.

He had accidents occasionally, for although he was careful, he worked under disadvantages on the jolting train. One day a bottle of phosphorus fell from its shelf and broke. The contents set the floor on fire. The fire was put out before it had done much injury; but the conductor was excited and angry. He said he would have no more of the dangerous stuff on his train. To be very sure that he would not, he threw the remaining bottles out of the car, and hurled after them not only all of the laboratory furnishings, but even the printing press. The owner protested with some spirit against the destruction of his property, whereupon the conductor seized him and pushed him out of the car.

Edison had learned in his rough-and-tumble life not to cry over spilt milk. It was discouraging to see the possessions he had collected with so much pains scattered by the roadside. But as soon as he had his fists unclinched the plucky fellow was ready to forgive the hasty conductor. "The old chap got a bad scare," he said to himself. "After all it's a wonder he didn't throw my traps overboard long ago." And he went to work picking up what was left of his printing shop and laboratory, planning the while where he would re-open his shop. He decided that his father's cellar would be the safest place. Before many days, he had made good his loss by new purchases and had begun work on a larger scale than ever.

Chapter 4

A Change of Business

E dison took up his train duties promptly, without any evidence of ill-feeling towards the conductor who had treated him so harshly. A few weeks after that unpleasant occurrence, the train stopped one morning at Mount Clemens, to take on some freight cars, which were waiting on the side track.

As usual, the train boy, with his papers under his arm, was peering about the station house to see what was going on. Suddenly, as he looked around the corner, he saw the two-year-old son of the station agent, playing on the track, while the heavy freight car that was being backed down to the train, was almost upon him. Without a second's hesitation, the newsboy threw his papers to the ground and plunged forward to save the child. With one flying leap he seized the boy and cleared the track, falling on the gravel beyond, just out of reach of the wheels of the car. The baggage-master, who saw the act and thought that both boys would be killed, gave a shriek which brought every one around the station to the spot.

When the child's father heard the story, he felt so grateful to the brave boy that he would have been glad to give him a rich reward. He was a poor man, however, and could not express his thanks in money. But there was one thing he could do, to better the boy's fortune. He was a good telegraph operator; he would teach young Edison telegraphing, and get him a position where he could earn twenty-five dollars a month. Taking the boy's hand, he said, "You have saved Jimmy's life, Al, and I'd like to show you how I feel about it. I haven't anything to give you, but if you'll stop off here two or three nights in the week I'll teach you to telegraph and get you a good job."

Edison's face lighted up with pleasure. "I don't want any pay for pulling Jimmy out from under that freight car," he said loftily. "But I would like mighty well to learn to telegraph. Nothing better! If it suits you we'll begin tonight."

The lessons were commenced at once and Mr. Mackenzie, the agent, found his work as instructor really pleasant at first. His pupil came regularly and made such surprising progress that it was a great satisfaction to teach him. But after a few days the train passed and "Al" did not get off. This happened several days in succession. Mr. Mackenzie felt disappointed. "I declare he's like all the rest of them," he mused. "I thought he had some grit. But I've always noticed that when a boy is so quick and learns so fast, he never keeps at it." He was mistaken, however, that time.

That very evening when the train came in, young Edison swung himself off with a beaming face. He carried a small package neatly tied up, which he was eager to show his friend. It proved to be a tiny telegraph instrument which he had made at a gunsmith's shop in Detroit. It was so small that it could be placed on a small envelope, yet it was perfectly complete, and worked well when tested.

The young student in telegraphy had not lost interest, but he had come to the place where he could get along without a regular teacher. He was used to doing things in his own way and at his own time, and having received a good start from Mr. Mackenzie, was able to go on without much further help from him. He had made friends with many of the telegraph operators along the railroad. He now visited their offices to practice his art. He found them all interested in his progress and ready to give him a word of advice when he needed it. In three months' time he had so thoroughly mastered the business that Mr. Mackenzie said the boy knew enough to teach him.

He was not satisfied with being able to work the instrument, to send and receive messages. His inquiring mind wanted to discover how the instrument worked and why. He immediately began to experiment with electricity in his cellar laboratory.

With the help of a friend he constructed a short telegraph line of his own. At first he tried to obtain a current from a very curious dynamo. He had noticed the sparks that may be produced by stroking a cat. Half in fun, and half in earnest, he got two large black cats and tried with much rubbing to create an electrical current, but was obliged to resort to the ordinary battery.

Edison gave up his position as train boy and spent most of his time at the Western Union Telegraph office in Port Huron. When there was more work to do than usual, or when one of the regular operators was not at his post, Edison was hired to work for a short time. He did good work and was soon given a regular position at a salary of twenty-five dollars a month, with the promise of additional pay for extra work.

Chapter 5

The Boy Telegraph Operator

E dison worked faithfully in his new position. He did extra work and did it well. But he waited in vain for the extra pay that had been promised him for taking long reports and working out of hours. When he found that the man who employed him did not keep his word, he gave up his position. Mr. Mackenzie soon got him a situation as night operator at Stratford, in Canada.

So far as ability to send and receive messages went, Edison was perfectly capable of filling the place. But he was by no means the slow, faithful, unquestioning, obedient agent to leave in charge of a telegraph office at night. He was a mere boy, only fifteen years of age, and had had no training in working under orders. He could not obey regulations which seemed to him useless, and he sometimes thought he could improve on the directions given him. There was no danger of his neglecting his duty through idleness, but he might neglect it while working out some pet notion of his own.

The manager of the circuit realized that the night operators might be tempted to shirk their work, and so he required them to telegraph a signal to him every half hour in order that he might be sure they were awake and at their posts. Edison's signal was six.

This was a wise regulation, but Edison did not appreciate the necessity for it. He found it a great bother to keep his eye on the clock and leave his reading or some experiment that he was working out in the quiet hours of night, to report that stupid "six" every thirty minutes. He wondered if he couldn't make a machine attached to the clock that would save him the trouble. After a good deal of thinking and experimenting, he fitted up an instrument that could telegraph "six" as well as he could.

This was a great relief to him, and he felt free to do what he liked with his time without much fear of discovery. He even left the office and made expeditions about town.

One night while he was away, the manager tried to call him up but could get no response. He thought this odd as Edison was more punctual with his signals than any other operator on the line. He waited, then tried again and again, with no better success, though the signals came with their accustomed regularity. He made an investigation, and the young inventor received a severe reprimand for his clever contrivance.

His next offense came near having serious results. He had orders to deliver messages to trains before reporting them back to the dispatcher. One evening, because it seemed easier to do so, he reversed the order and returned the message before delivering it. Then he heard the engine bell ring for the train to start. He jumped up in a hurry, but when he got to the platform, the train was well in motion. The message was an order for the train to wait at the switch until a special had passed. He ran frantically after the train hoping he might catch it at the freight depot, but he could not overtake it.

He ran swiftly back to telegraph his error to the dispatcher, only to learn that it was too late to warn the other train. Now because of his disobedience two great trains were rushing towards each other on the same track. That was a terrible hour for the poor boy. There were chances that the engineers would see each other's engines in time to prevent a wreck; but there were chances that they would not. It was frightful to think of the misery and loss he might be responsible for.

The watchfulness of the engineers prevented a collision. When the special came thundering up the track safe and sound, Edison knew that the danger was over. His disobedience had brought no harm to others, but he felt sure that he would hear more of it.

Nor was he mistaken. The superintendent called him to his office and frightened him with threats of imprisonment. He left town on the next train without even collecting the money due him for his services.

His experience at Stratford had been unfortunate perhaps, but he was a better operator because of it. He had not only gained in skill, but had learned the importance of obedience in little things.

He spent a few weeks at home out of work. One day

when he was down by the St. Clair river, watching the ice which was breaking and piling up across the stream, word came that the electric cable between Port Huron and Sarnia, the Canadian city on the opposite side of the river, had been broken by the ice jam. There was no bridge; the ferryboat could not run on the ice-blocked river; with the cable broken all communication between the places was stopped.

Edison saw a locomotive standing on a track near by, and a thought struck him. He jumped aboard her and whistled a greeting to Sarnia, making short toots for the dots and long toots for the dashes. He repeated his message several times. At last the trained ear of the old operator in Sarnia recognized the familiar signals of the Morse alphabet, and with the help of an engine whistle, sent a reply across the impassable river.

This little incident was very much talked about. People began to say that Thomas Edison was most ingenious.

Good telegraph operators were hard to get, and Edison was not long without a position.

Chapter 6

Telegrapher and Inventor

E dison was not a dreamer. He may have had vague notions of doing something great in the distant future, but they did not interfere with the accomplishment of his practical, definite ideas. Having become a telegraph operator, his modest ambition was to be a good one. More than that, he wanted to be able to receive "press reports." That is, he wanted to be able to work so fast that he could handle the long dispatches sent to the newspapers.

That was not an easy task. Indeed for a while he gave up hope of being able to keep up with the clickings of an expert sender, without the help of some mechanical device. If he could only find a way to make those confusing dots and dashes come more slowly!

His busy brain and nimble fingers working together, soon discovered a way to do this. He contrived a repeating receiver, which recorded the message as rapidly as the best sender could send it, and repeated it as slowly as the poorest receiver could wish.

When this repeater was in working order, Edison

secured an engagement to take some press-report work. He told the sender to "rush" him. The man did so, but no matter how rapidly he worked, he did not seem to be able to confuse the marvelous receiver. Edison was meanwhile copying slowly from his faithful repeater. He was able in this way to hand in beautifully written, unscratched, and unblotted sheets of report, which aroused the astonishment and admiration of all who saw them.

Soon, however, a report came in that had to be delivered immediately. Then the inventor was in difficulty, and had to admit that he was not such a fast receiver as he seemed.

To invent the repeater, required a higher order of mind perhaps, than was necessary to receive messages rapidly. But Edison felt no pride in that achievement. His object was to be a rapid receiver and nothing else would satisfy him.

He next made a series of thorough experiments in penmanship, to discover which was the most rapid style of writing. After a long and careful examination he decided on the clear, round, upright characters which he used all the rest of his life. It is interesting to notice that this youth was about thirty years ahead of the writing teachers in adopting the beautiful vertical writing, which is taught in many schools today.

Obliged to give up press-report work until he had gained greater skill, Edison devoted his time to practicing as the only means of acquiring the speed he desired. He worked all day and, whenever he could get employment, all night, snatching bits of sleep when he could. His constant diligence soon enabled him to work so fast that he was put at one end of a line worked by a Louisville operator, who was one of the fastest senders in the country. His experience at that wire made him as expert as even he desired to be.

But he was not ready to sit down to rest. As soon as one thing became easy for Edison he always began working on something else.

While at Memphis, he constructed an instrument called an automatic repeater, which made it possible to connect separate telegraph lines in such a way as to transfer messages from one wire to the other without the aid of an operator.

He then began to try to discover how two messages might be sent over the same wire at the same time. He spent a large part of his time reading and experimenting with this end in view.

His fellow operators laughed at him and called him the "luny," because he had so many "queer notions" and did not care for the things they enjoyed. He worked constantly, dressed shabbily, and spent most of his money for scientific books and materials with which to make experiments. His gay comrades like him in spite of his peculiarities. He was ready with jokes and funny stories, and could be depended on to lend an empty-pocketed friend a dollar in the days of scarcity which usually preceded pay day.

His employers were often impatient with him. They thought it strange that a young man who could telegraph so well, was not content to do it, but must needs neglect his work, while he wasted time and kept the office in confusion with some impossible scheme.

This is the reason that for five years Edison roamed from town to town, through the central states, never having much trouble to get a place because he was such a good operator, and never keeping one long because he could not overcome his impulse to invent.

During those five years he suffered a good many hardships and formed very irregular habits of work, often studying and working all night long. But while many of his comrades fell into evil ways, Edison lived a clean, straight life. This was one reason why he was able to work so hard without injuring his health.

Chapter 7

In Boston

E dison had a friend in Boston. This man urged him to come East. He said that he would receive a better salary and have greater opportunities for study and invention. When a vacancy occurred in the Boston office, he recommended Edison for the place. And so it happened that when Edison was twenty-one years old, he was called to the great city of Boston.

Here is the account the inventor himself gives of his first appearance in the Boston telegraph office:

"I had been four days and nights on the road, and, having had very little sleep, did not present a very fresh or stylish appearance, especially as compared to the operators of the East, who were far more dressy than their brethren of the West. The manager asked me when I was ready to go to work. 'Now,' I replied. I was then told to return at 5:50 P.M., and punctually at that hour I entered the main operating rooms, and was introduced to the night manager. My peculiar appearance caused much mirth, and, as I afterwards learnt, the night operators consulted together how they might 'put a job on the jay from the woolly West.' I was given a pen and assigned the New York No. 1 wire.

"After waiting upwards of one hour I was told to come over to a special table, and take a special report for the *Boston Herald*, the conspirators having arranged to have one of the fastest senders in New York to send the dispatch and 'salt' the new man. I sat down unsuspiciously at the table and the New York man started slowly. I had long since perfected myself in a simple and rapid style of handwriting, devoid of flourishes, and susceptible of being increased from forty-five to fifty-four words a minute by gradually reducing the size of the lettering. This was several words faster than any other operator in the United States.

"Soon the New York man increased his speed, to which I easily adapted my pace. This put my rival on his mettle, and he put on his best powers, which, however, were soon reached. At this point I happened to look up, and saw the operators all looking over my shoulder, with their faces shining with fun and excitement. I knew then that they were trying to put a job on me, but kept my own counsel and went on placidly with my work, even sharpening a pencil at intervals, by way of extra aggravation.

"The New York man then commenced to slur over his words, running them together, and sticking the signals; but I had been used to this style of telegraphy in taking reports and was not in the least discomfited. Finally when I thought the fun had gone far enough, and having about completed the special, I quietly opened the key and remarked, 'Say, young man, change off, and send with your other foot.' This broke the New York man all up, and he turned the job over to another man to finish."

Men are usually ready to respect real merit. Edison's fellow-workers, on discovering his ability, gave the new comer a cordial welcome among them, in spite of his careless dress.

But better even than that, Edison found his new employer to be a man of high intelligence. He could talk over his ideas with him without fear of being called a "luny." It was a new pleasure to the young man to find sympathy and appreciation concerning the questions that were of the highest interest to him.

The Boston Public Library furnished him with valuable works which he had not been able to obtain in the West. He met men of scientific learning and came in contact with highly skilled artisans.

Everything in his new life stimulated his ambition and encouraged him to attempt great things. Much of the time he felt as he expressed it one morning to a friend: "I've got so much to do and life is so short, I'm going to hustle."

His regular work occupied the night hours. That left the day free. He spent as few as possible of the precious hours in sleep. Having found that he could not carry on his experiments in the telegraph office here, as he had so often done in the West, he opened a small shop of his own. In that shop he spent a large part of each day. Sometimes he devoted all of his time to working on his own inventions. Again, he took orders and did work for others.

He became known in Boston as an authority on electricity, and was even invited to speak on the subject before a school of young women.

He was especially interested at this time in inventing an electrical instrument for recording votes in a great assembly like the House of Representatives. He made an excellent machine that did its work faultlessly, and had it patented. After all his labor and expense he found that legislative bodies did not care for such an accurate and speedy vote recorder. His invention was useless. This was a bitter disappointment to him and he did not forget the lesson it taught him: never invent anything without first finding out whether it is needed.

Having failed with his vote recorder because of his ignorance of parliamentary customs, he returned to the familiar field of telegraphy and once more tried to solve the problem of sending two messages over a wire at one time. There was no doubt that a contrivance which would make that possible would be in demand.

He progressed so well with his experiments that in 1869 he was ready to make a trial of his invention on a large scale.

At this time his engagement with the Western Union Telegraph Company being completed, he resolved to go to New York.

Chapter 8

Recognized as an Electrician

E dison's stay in Boston had been pleasant and profitable in many ways, but he felt more and more that New York, the great center of the American business world, was the city of opportunity.

He arrived there with no work and no money. For although he had been a hard worker while in Boston, he had spent so much on experiments and inventions that he was heavily in debt. He did not feel worried for the future, however, He had the greatest confidence in himself and in electricity. He knew that electricity could be made to do marvelous things and that few men knew so well as he how to make it do them.

Failing to get employment in a telegraph office as he had hoped to do, he wandered about, visiting the various establishments maintained in connection with electrical enterprises, in the hope of finding some work. One day as he approached the office of Laws' Gold Reporting Telegraph Company, he noticed an excited crowd of men and messenger boys around the entrance. Coming nearer, he learned that there was something wrong with the electrical instrument which sent the market reports to the brokers' offices, and that if it was not remedied at once, many business men would lose heavily.

He made his way quietly and quickly into the office where he found Mr. Laws almost distracted with anxiety. The apparatus refused to work, and he was so nervous and excited that he could not find what the trouble was. Edison went up, and introducing himself as an electrician, made a rapid but careful investigation. He had been working on an invention somewhat similar and understood the instrument perfectly. He discovered the difficulty and corrected it while Mr. Laws looked on in admiration. His sure, swift movements showed his familiarity with the complicated and delicate mechanism.

This performance won the respect of Mr. Laws as completely as the rapid telegraphing had secured the esteem of the Boston operators. Mr. Laws not only felt grateful, but he immediately recognized in Edison a man whose services were worth having. This incident led to Edison's obtaining regular employment under Mr. Laws at a salary of three hundred dollars a month.

Having accomplished his boyish ambition to be an expert telegraph operator, Edison, at the age of twenty-two gave up that business and started out in a broader field of work. He began at once to make improvements in the machine used by the company he served. Before long he invented a new and better instrument to take its place.

His next important step was to enter the service of the Gold and Stock Telegraph Company. Edison made numerous inventions in connection with the apparatus used by this company. The company considered them so valuable that it offered to buy them all. When the committee representing the company asked Edison how much he would take for his inventions he replied that he did not know what they were worth. He asked what the company was willing to give him. He had decided to accept if offered five thousand dollars. Imagine his surprise when offered forty thousand dollars.

The young man was not long in deciding how to spend his unexpectedly acquired fortune. With it he equipped a larger more elaborate shop than he had ever had. He now had room, implements, and assistants for working out the schemes which had been simmering in his head ever since he was a boy.

He accomplished so much that he began to be looked upon as a wonder. The Western Union Telegraph Company and the Gold and Stock Telegraph Company feared that rival companies would obtain the use of his patents. So they paid him a large salary to give them the option on all of his telegraphic inventions. This made it possible for Edison to devote his entire time to the work he loved: to making machines which would do well the work which existing machines did poorly.

Chapter 9

Inventor and Manufacturer

E dison opened a large laboratory and factory in Newark, New Jersey. There he employed three hundred men to assist him in his experiments and to make the contrivances which he invented.

This was a more serious responsibility than he had yet undertaken. It was one thing to tinker away by himself and work out his ideas with his own skillful hands, and quite another to manage and direct three hundred men.

He was not, however, ignorant of human nature. Even when a newsboy he had been busy getting acquainted with people and learning to influence them so they would do as he wished.

In his factory his manner toward his men was friendly and boyishly unconstrained. There was little formality between employer and employees; his men were not afraid of the "boss." He depended on their interest and good-will, rather than obedience to rigid rules, for the best results. His big factory was managed with a surprising lack of regularity. If he was anxious to have a piece of work finished all hands were kept over hours.

When things went well and some important undertaking was completed, there was a fragment of a holiday.

It is said that when a man asked Edison to what he owed his success, he replied, "To never looking at the clock." He expected from his men something of the same indifference to time and absorption in work that he had always shown.

On one occasion, when an instrument did not give satisfaction and he could not find what was wrong, he took half a dozen of his most able assistants with him to an upper room, saying, "We will stay there until this thing is straightened out." They worked there sixty hours, and at the end of that time came out of their voluntary prison tired, but satisfied and successful.

If Edison demanded a good deal of his men, he was more severe with himself. Many and many a time, after a day's work, he sat all night in his private office or laboratory studying out some baffling problem.

He was very much beloved by his workmen, and if he came back from a business trip to New York, with his boyish face all aglow with satisfaction, and tossed his silk hat up to the ceiling with a cheer for the invention he had just sold, a wave of good feeling and hilarity spread over the whole establishment.

It was in the first year of his life at Newark that Edison married. After a brief and business-like courtship, he married Miss Mary Stillwell, a young woman employed in his factory. He carried his enthusiasm for electricity even into his home and nicknamed his first two children

"Dot" and "Dash," from the signals of the telegraph.

In money matters Edison was as reckless as in his expense of time. He employed no bookkeeper, and paid his bills with notes. He rarely knew whether he was in debt or had a surplus on hand. In his view, money was merely a means for carrying on the work that was for him the one important thing in life, and he rarely worried about it. He had good reason to have a feeling of security; for it is said that before leaving Newark, he had at one time forty-five distinct inventions in varying stages of completion, and, that the profit arising from their sale amounted to four hundred thousand dollars.

His most important achievement at Newark was the perfecting of the quadruplex telegraph, by means of which not only two but four messages could be sent over one wire at the same instant. Besides this, so many minor inventions were completed that Edison was called "The young man who keeps the path to the patent office hot with his footsteps."

Patent Office at Washington

Chapter 10

The Wizard of Menlo Park

I t is probable that when Edison opened his laboratory at Newark he felt that it would be some time before he outgrew that. In 1876, however, his work as an inventor had developed so wonderfully that he decided to give up manufacturing and devote his time wholly to inventing.

He needed a more extensive laboratory, one situated in a place so out of the way of public travel that he would not have many visitors. For the site of his new laboratory, he chose Menlo Park. The name has since come to be so closely associated with Edison that when we hear it mentioned we think of the phonograph, the telephone, the electric light, and all of the great inventions which were worked out there.

It was a quiet spot, about an hour's ride by railroad from New York City, where the inventor was frequently called on business. Here in an open expanse Edison had a modest dwelling and a vast laboratory erected.

This laboratory, a plain white frame structure was far from being a handsome building. Its owner's only

In the Laboratory

wish was to have it spacious, well-lighted and convenient. He spared no cost in fitting it up with the most improved mechanical apparatus for experimenting. He had a powerful engine to supply the force needed.

The workshop, a room one hundred feet long, was enough to delight the heart of a lover of fine machinery. There were great whirring, buzzing wheels, endless belts of strongest leather, beautifully finished lathes, milling machines, drills, and planers. There were all sorts of electrical machinery, splendidly made and kept bright and shining. But there were no electric lights and no telephone in the great laboratory unless, perhaps, in the mind of the inventor.

Upstairs was a chemical laboratory, a laboratory far beyond the brightest dreams of the newsboy on the Grand Trunk Railroad. Its walls were lined with shelves laden with rows of mysterious jars and bottles. The inventor made it a rule to keep at hand some of every chemical substance known. There were blowpipes, retorts, test tubes, and flasks without number.

Besides these rooms, there was a library. It was a large one well filled with standard and modern scientific works.

There was a small band of well organized workers at Menlo Park. It included skilled mechanics, with a director at their head; scientific experimenters, with a scholarly professor at their head; a mathematician, a private secretary, and even a bookkeeper.

Guiding and controlling all, was Edison, the wonder worker, who could catch the lightning and hold it imprisoned in tiny glass globes, who could make it possible for one man to hear another talking hundreds of miles away, who could measure the heat of the stars, who could make a machine that would talk and sing and laugh like a human voice.

This man of almost magical powers, who worked at all hours of the night in the lonely laboratory, whence the sound of explosions, and flashes of light more brilliant than sunlight, often issued, began to be regarded almost with a feeling of awe. People called him the "Wizard of Menlo Park."

To those who worked with Mr. Edison, there was nothing awe-inspiring about him. He was not in the least spoiled by his success. He respected all parts of the work to which he had given his devotion, and the man who did the humblest portion of it well, was esteemed by him. He was not afraid of hard work himself, and although he had competent men to manage the business for him, always took an active part in the affairs of the shop. He went about in rusty work clothes stained with acids, and with hands discolored and scarred, inspecting everything, and lending a hand where things were not going just as he wished. Menlo Park was no place for a man who did not love his work so much that he could forget his personal appearance and comfort while busy.

On one occasion a new man refused to perform a task which Mr. Edison had directed him to do. He said that he had not accepted the position with a view of becoming a manual laborer. Mr. Edison with extreme courtesy begged his pardon, for having made an unreasonable request, and then did the work himself. That made the young man feel uncomfortable, but it taught him the lesson which all of Mr. Edison's employees had to learn sooner or later—the lesson of self-forgetfulness in work.

In the management of his business Mr. Edison had conformed in many ways to ordinary business methods. But hours at Menlo Park were almost as irregular as at Newark. The inventor could not get over the belief that the man who never got so interested in his work that he failed to hear the twelve o'clock whistle at noon, or the six o'clock whistle at night, was a poor sort of fellow. For his own part, he had not outgrown his independence of the clock.

As the years passed, the inventor's mind lost nothing of its youthful activity. He found it easy to keep every one in the big laboratory busy working out his ideas. Whenever he thought of a possible improvement in one of his own inventions, or in a contrivance made by someone else, he made a note of it in a thick blank book. When one piece of work was finished this book always suggested innumerable ideas for further undertakings.

Sometimes Edison's inventions were pushed forward with amazing rapidity. An idea would occur to him in the morning. His draughtsmen would draw up the plans for it, and the workmen would make it in a single day.

He tells an incident to show how quickly he was able to transact patent business, not only at Washington, but in London: He made a discovery at four in the afternoon, telegraphed to his solicitor, and had him draw up the necessary specifications at once. Then cabled to London, an application for a patent, and before he arose next morning received word that his application had been filed in the English patent office. To understand this speedy transaction, we must remember that while it was early morning at Menlo Park it was noonday at London.

Chapter 11

Inventions

W hile numerous small inventions were thought of, made, and patented in an almost incredibly short space of time, you must not think that Edison never had any hindrances or difficulties. There were inventions on which he and his assistants labored for years, spending tens of thousands of dollars before reaching satisfactory results.

It would take too long to name all of Edison's inventions, and it would be impossible to describe them all. There are very few departments of electrical invention to which he has not contributed something. The electric railroad and the automobile have received a share of his thought. His telephone; the megaphone, which carries the sound of the voice great distances without the help of wires; the quadruplex telegraph; the tasimeter, which measures the heat of the stars; or the kinetoscope,—any one of them would have made the inventor famous. But he is perhaps best known by the invention of the incandescent electric light and the phonograph.

Every American boy and girl has Edison's name closely associated with the brilliant little globes of light which are seen by thousands along city streets, in churches, in theaters, in public halls, and even in private dwellings.

A traveler in far off Egypt asked an ignorant donkey boy if he had ever heard of the President of the United States. He had not. He next asked if he had ever heard of Edison. With a nod of intelligence the boy pointed to the electric light before the door of the hotel for answer.

Edison once said that the electric light had cost him more time, anxiety, and expense than any other invention. It was, however, the invention which made him independently rich.

The principle of the light is simple. When an electric current passes from a good conductor to a poor one it causes heat. That a bright light might be obtained by non-conducting substances heated in this way, had been known for many years, but no one before Edison was able to turn the knowledge to practical use.

Even Edison found it extremely difficult to make an inexpensive, durable, and strong light. The greatest difficulty was to find a non-conducting filament strong enough to endure, and slight enough to be heated to a white glow with a moderate charge of electricity.

Those will never forget it, who were present at Menlo Park when the search for the filament was begun. Experiment after experiment failed, while the "wizard," growing only more wide awake and resolute, begged his associates, "Let us make one before we sleep."

Expeditions were made to Japan, India, Africa, and South America in search of the best possible material for the filament.

Men were unwilling to believe that the incandescent electric light could be used extensively for illuminating purposes. But in the winter of 1880, a public exhibit of the new invention was given at Menlo Park. The streets and trees were brilliantly lighted, and the laboratory was aglow inside and out with the dazzling white lights. Special trains were run to Menlo Park. Hundreds of people went to see the novel spectacle and all who saw were convinced that the incandescent light was a success.

The phonograph, while not so familiar to us as the electric light, arouses our wonder even more. You have perhaps heard that sound is made by vibrations of air. You have shouted in a bare room and heard the echo of your words come back with startling distinctness. The wall received the vibrations and sent back other vibrations making similar but somewhat blurred sounds. This repetition of the vibrations to get a repetition of sound is the principle on which the phonograph is based.

Edison gives an interesting account of the dawning of the idea in his mind. He says: "I was singing to the mouthpiece of a telephone, when the vibrations of the voice sent the fine steel point into my finger. That set me to thinking. If I could record the actions of the point and send the point over the same surface afterward, I saw no reason why the thing would not talk. I tried the experiment first on a strip of telegraph paper, and found that the point made an alphabet. I shouted the words 'Halloo! Halloo!' into the mouthpiece, ran the paper back

Each Phonograph bears my signature without it no other machine is genuine

Thomas A. Edison

over the steel point, and heard a faint 'Halloo! Halloo!' in return. I determined to make a machine that would work accurately, and gave my assistants instructions, telling them what I had discovered."

Chapter 12

At Orange, New Jersey

I n 1886 a new laboratory was built at Orange, New Jersey. This laboratory is so large that it makes its famous predecessor at Menlo Park seem small and insignificant, by comparison. The equipment is complete for carrying on all sorts of experiments from those relating to the kinetograph to those in connection with the magnetic-ore separator.

In building his laboratory the inventor remembered to provide in many ways for the comfort and pleasure of the men whom he employed. At the top of the building there is a large lecture hall. There the men often assemble to listen to scientific lectures given by the best scholars and lecturers in the country.

The library, with its wealth of books, is an attractive room. Mr. Edison cares little for luxury or ease, and this room was at first as plain as the rest of the building. But on his forty-second birthday his men surprised him by introducing into his library some of the comforts he never thought of providing for himself. Rugs, easy chairs, tables, pictures, even plants were used to give the room

The Laboratory at Orange

an air of comfort and beauty.

In this room the inventor sometimes sits, not reading at his ease, but surrounded by great stacks of books on some particular subject, glancing eagerly through one volume after another as if his life depended on his mastering their contents within a given time. He respects books as the record of the labor of other students and scientists. But he is often disappointed in them; he says, "Some way I never find just what I want in books."

During his early manhood, Edison contributed little in person to the social side of life. He believed that in his inventions he gave to the world the best part of himself. Society accepted the inventions but was not satisfied. Men insist on considering a man greater than any machine he may make. Everything Edison did only made people more anxious to see and know him. For a

A Corner in the Library

long time he rebuffed all efforts of the public to make a hero of him. When an attempt was made to give a dinner in honor of the great inventor he refused to be present saying: "One hundred thousand dollars would not tempt me to sit through two hours of personal glorification."

Efforts have been made to induce him to talk into one of his phonographs. But he refuses emphatically, declaring, "It would make me sick with disgust to see on every corner, 'Put a nickel in the slot and hear Edison talk.'"

He has not worked in order that he may at one time live without work. He says that his highest pleasure is in work and he looks forward to no season of rest. Although he is so devoted to his work, Edison's life is not void of brightness. He is one of the most joyous men in the world. Failures and disappointments, he has accepted through

Edison's Home in Llewellyn Park

life as philosophically as he did the destruction of his first laboratory by the angry railroad conductor.

He has the rare ability of transferring his attention quickly from one thing to another. When exhausted with work, he will dash out of his office, tell a funny story, have a good laugh with a friend, and in five minutes be as hard at work as ever. He keeps an organ in his library on which he has taught himself to play a few of his favorite airs, and this often affords him a few minutes' refreshment in the midst of hours of close study.

His work never loses its charm; he is always engaged in some novel and interesting experiment. Within the last few years, however, he has admitted some pleasures into his life not directly connected with his work. Mr. Edison has traveled extensively in America and in

Europe and been received with high honors everywhere. His first wife having died, he married again, and bought a beautiful and luxurious home in Llewellyn Park, near Orange, New Jersey.

Afterword

Thomas Alva Edison obtained his last patent, his 1,093rd, at the age of 83. It is a record no one has beaten yet. He died the next year (1931), waking long enough to tell his wife Mina, "It is very beautiful over there." Homes and factories and shops all over America dimmed their lights in his honor on the evening of the day he was laid to rest.

Appendix

Compiled and Annotated
by John Shafer

Images provided by The Thomas Edison Papers at Rutgers University.

Thomas Edison in 1878, just two years before he applied for the Electric-Lamp Patent.

Appendix

Many of the ideas that Thomas Edison conceived, he worked on over a number of years, filing additional patents as he improved or enhanced the design. It sometimes took a year or more for the Patent Office to grant his patent.

He would work on multiple projects at once, so ideas from one project would often find their way into other projects.

Here are just a few of Edison's more than 1,000 patent sketches and explanations.

Pages 62 and 63: The first Electric-Lamp patent, the first of many patents on the light.

Pages 64 and 65: Two years later he had an idea to make the light recyclable. The lamp could be disassembled to replace the filament.

T. A. EDISON.
Electric-Lamp.

No. 223,898.   Patented Jan. 27, 1880.

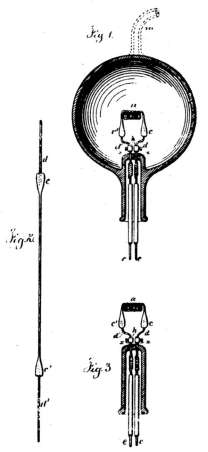

Witnesses
Chas H Smith
Geo T. Pinckney

Inventor
Thomas A. Edison
for Lemuel W. Serrell

SimplyCharlotteMason.com

UNITED STATES PATENT OFFICE.

THOMAS A. EDISON, OF MENLO PARK, NEW JERSEY

ELECTRIC LAMP.

SPECIFICATION forming part of Letters Patent No. 223,898, dated January 27, 1880.

Application filed November 4, 1879.

To all whom it may concern:

Be it known that I, THOMAS ALVA EDISON, of Menlo Park, in the State of New Jersey, United States of America, have invented an Improvement in Electric Lamps, and in the method of manufacturing the same, (Case No. 186,) of which the following is a specification.

The object of this invention is to produce electric lamps giving light by incandescence, which lamps shall have high resistance, so as to allow of the practical subdivision of the electric light.

The invention consists in a light-giving body of carbon wire or sheets coiled or arranged in such a manner as to offer great resistance to the passage of the electric current, and at the same time present but a slight surface from which radiation can take place.

The invention further consists in placing such burner of great resistance in a nearly-perfect vacuum, to prevent oxidation and injury to the conductor by the atmosphere. The current is conducted into the vacuum-bulb through platina wires sealed into the glass.

The invention further consists in the method of manufacturing carbon conductors of high resistance, so as to be suitable for giving light by incandescence, and in the manner of securing perfect contact between the metallic conductors or leading-wires and the carbon conductor.

Heretofore light by incandescence has been obtained from rods of carbon of one to four ohms resistance, placed in closed vessels, in which the atmospheric air has been replaced by gases that do not combine chemically with the carbon. The vessel holding the burner has been composed of glass cemented to a metallic base. The connection between the leading wires and the carbon has been obtained by clamping the carbon to the metal. The leading-wires have always been large, so that their resistance shall be many times less than the burner, and, in general, the attempts of previous persons have been to reduce the resistance of the carbon rod. The disadvantages of following this practice are, that a lamp having but one to four ohms resistance cannot be worked in great numbers in multiple arc without the employment of main conductors of enormous dimensions; that, owing to the low resistance of the lamp, the leading-wires must be of large

dimensions and good conductors, and a glass globe cannot be kept tight at the place where the wires pass in and are cemented; hence the carbon is consumed, because there must be almost a perfect vacuum to render the carbon stable, especially when such carbon is small in mass and high in electrical resistance.

The use of a gas in the receiver at the atmospheric pressure, although not attacking the carbon, serves to destroy it in time by "air-washing," or the attrition produced by the rapid passage of the air over the slightly-coherent highly-heated surface of the carbon. I have reversed this practice. I have discovered that even a cotton thread properly carbonized and placed in a sealed glass bulb exhausted to one-millionth of an atmosphere offers from one hundred to five hundred ohms resistance to the passage of the current, and that it is absolutely stable at very high temperatures; that if the thread be coiled as a spiral and carbonized, or if any fibrous vegetable substance which will leave a carbon residue after heating in a closed chamber be so coiled, as much as two thousand ohms resistance may be obtained without presenting a radiating-surface greater than three-sixteenths of an inch; that if such fibrous material be rubbed with a plastic composed of lamp-black and tar, its resistance may be made high or low, according to the amount of lamp-black placed upon it; that carbon filaments may be made by a combination of tar and lamp-black, the latter being previously ignited in a closed crucible for several hours and afterward moistened and kneaded until it assumes the consistency of thick putty. Small pieces of this material may be rolled out in the form of wire as small as seven one-thousandths of a inch in diameter and over a foot in length, and the same may be coated with a non-conducting non-carbonizing substance and wound on a bobbin, or as a spiral, and the tar carbonized in a closed chamber by subjecting it to high heat, the spiral after carbonization retaining its form.

All these forms are fragile and cannot be clamped to the leading wires with sufficient force to insure good contact and prevent heating. I have discovered that if platinum wires are used and the plastic lamp-black and tar material be molded around it in the act of carbonization there is an intimate union by com-

T. A. EDISON.

INCANDESCENT ELECTRIC LAMP.

No. 264,657.   Patented Sept. 19, 1882.

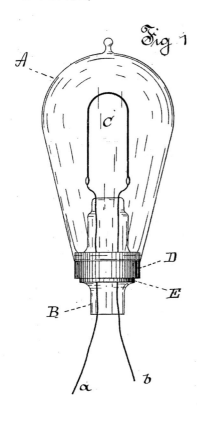

Fig. 1

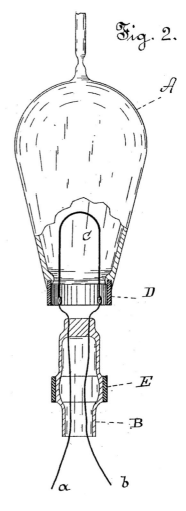

Fig. 2.

WITNESSES:

O. D. Mott

M. J. Clayeth.

INVENTOR:

T. A. Edison

BY Dyer & Wilber

ATTORNEYS.

UNITED STATES PATENT OFFICE.

THOMAS A. EDISON, OF MENLO PARK, NEW JERSEY, ASSIGNOR TO THE
EDISON ELECTRIC LIGHT COMPANY, OF NEW YORK, N. Y.

INCANDESCENT ELECTRIC LAMP.

SPECIFICATION forming part of Letters Patent No. 264,657, dated September 19, 1882.

Application filed August 30, 1881. (No model.)

To all whom it may concern:

Be it known that I, THOMAS A. EDISON, of Menlo Park, in the county of Middlesex and State of New Jersey, have invented a new and
5 useful Improvement in Incandescent Electric Lamps, (Case No. 322;) and I do hereby declare that the following is a full and exact description of the same, reference being had to the accompanying drawings, and to the let-
10 ters of reference marked thereon.

The object I have in view is to produce another form of incandescing electric lamp, which can be taken apart when the carbon is destroyed and the principal parts again util-
15 ized. This I accomplish by providing the lower end or neck of the glass bulb or globe with a ring of platinum, which is sealed into the glass of the globe and is soldered to another platinum ring sealed into the glass of
20 the wire-support. After the platinum rings are soldered together the globe is exhausted and sealed. When the carbon is broken the platinum rings can be separated by melting the solder by heat or eating it away with
25 acid, and the parts can be used over again, it being only necessary to supply a new carbon filament, to solder the platinum rings together again, and to re-exhaust and reseal the globe. For this last purpose the globe will
30 be heated at the top, and will be perforated and provided with a glass tube for making connection with a suitable exhausting apparatus.

In the drawings, Figure 1 is a view of the
35 lamp complete, and Fig. 2 a vertical section of the two parts of the lamp before the platinum rings are soldered together.

A is the glass globe; B, the glass wire-support; C, the carbon filament, and *a b* the lead-
40 ing-in wires. D is a platinum ring, sealed to the glass at the lower end of the neck of the globe, and E is another platinum ring, which is dropped over the upper end of the glass wire-support, and sealed to the glass of the
45 enlarged portion of the wire-support. One of these rings is preferably smaller than the other, so that they fit closely one over the other. These platinum rings are soldered together

before the lamp is exhausted. To separate the two glass portions of the lamp the solder can 50 be melted or eaten away by acid.

It will be understood that the tubular glass wire-support B is hermetically sealed at its upper end by being flattened and fused upon the leading-in wires *a b*, such leading-in wires 55 passing out through this tube. After the globe A is hermetically sealed at its lower end, and secured to the support B by the soldering of the platinum rings D E together, the lamp is exhausted by means of the glass tube 60 attached to the globe, which is sealed off by fusion of the glass. The joints between the platinum rings and the two glass portions of the lamp are made air-tight by the fusion of the glass upon such rings. 65

What I claim is—

1. In an incandescing electric lamp, the combination, with the two portions of the lamp made entirely of glass, of a joint between said parts, composed of two platinum portions at- 70 tached to the glass parts by the fusion of the glass upon them, said platinum portions being hermetically secured together, substantially as specified.

2. In an incandescing electric lamp, the com- 75 bination of the two portions of the lamp made entirely of glass, the carbon filament supported from one of said glass portions by leading-in wires passing through and sealed into the glass by the fusion of the glass thereon, 80 and a separable metallic joint between the two glass portions of the lamp, substantially as specified.

3. In an incandescing electric lamp, the combination of the two glass portions with the lamp, 85 of the carbon filament supported from one of said glass portions by leading-in wires passing through and sealed into the glass by the fusion of the glass thereon, a sealed glass exhausting-tube on one of said glass portions, 90 and a separable metallic joint between the two portions of the lamp, substantially as specified.

4. In an incandescing electric lamp, the combination, with the glass globe A, of a tubular 95 glass wire-support, B, extending up into the

2   264,657

globe and hermetically sealed at its upper end upon the leading-in wires, and the platinum rings D E, secured to the lower end of the globe and to the sides of said tubular sup-
5 port by the fusion of the glass upon said rings, such rings being secured together to form a separable air-tight joint, substantially as specified.

This specification signed and witnessed this 21st day of May, 1881.

THOMAS A. EDISON.

Witnesses:
RICHD. N. DYER,
H. W. SEELY.

Pages 67–71: Edison developed a lot of ideas around the telegraph. He worked on making it transmit the same message to multiple locations, and he developed an automated telegraph that was so fast, he had to invent a way to record the transmissions so they could be recalled and jotted down. This is what later became the phonograph.

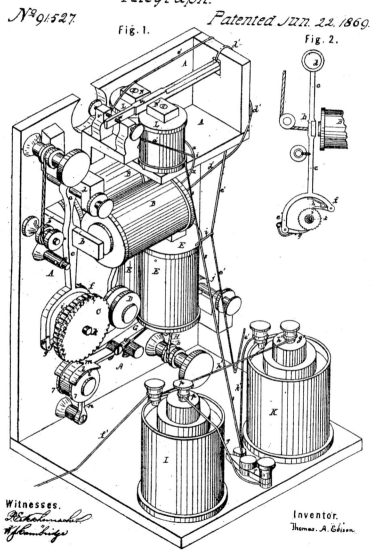

T. A. Edison.

Telegraph.

Nº 91.527.

Patented Jun. 22. 1869.

Fig. 1.

Fig. 2.

Witnesses.

Inventor.

Thomas. A. Edison

T. A. Edison.
Telegraph.

Patented Jun. 22, 1869.

Nº 91,527.

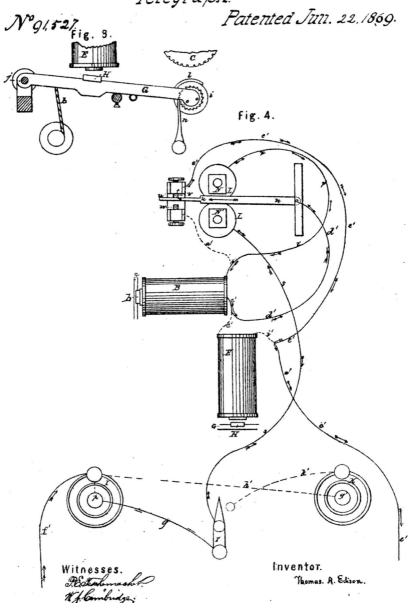

Fig. 9.

C

Fig. 4.

Witnesses.

Inventor.

Thomas. A. Edison.

T. A. Edison.
Telegraph.

No 91.527. Patented Jun. 22. 1869.

Fig. 5.

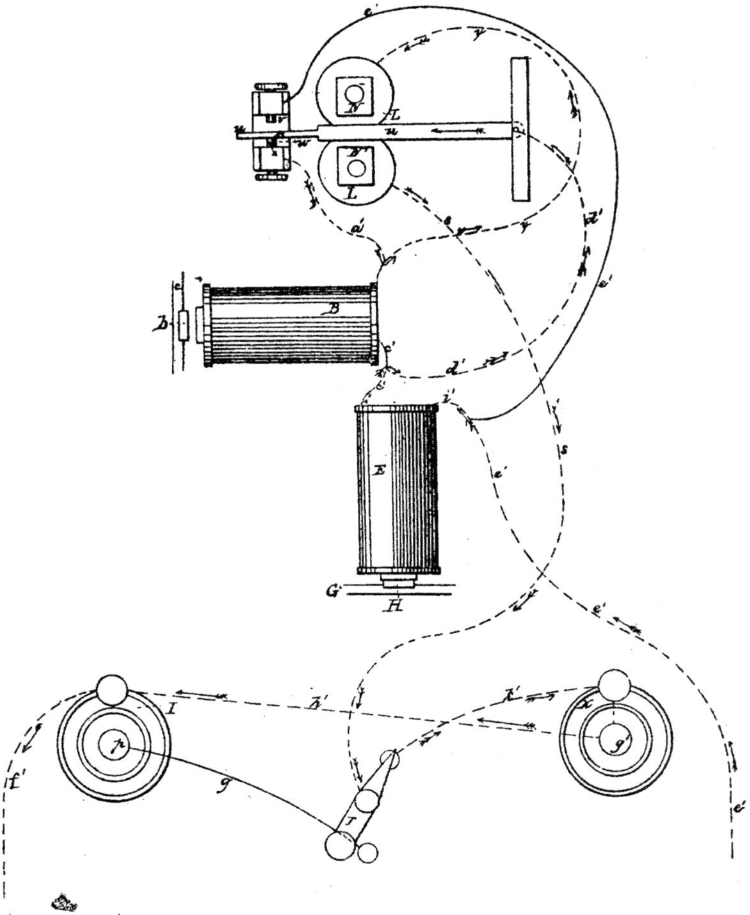

Witnesses.
P. E. Teschemacher.
W. J. Cambridge.

Inventor.
Thomas A. Edison

UNITED STATES PATENT OFFICE.

THOMAS A. EDISON, OF BOSTON, ASSIGNOR TO JOEL H. HILLS AND WM. E. PLUMMER, OF NEWTON, MASSACHUSETTS.

IMPROVEMENT IN PRINTING-TELEGRAPHS.

Specification forming part of Letters Patent No. **91,527**, dated June 22, 1869.

To all whom it may concern:

Be it known that I, THOMAS A. EDISON, of Boston, in the county of Suffolk and State of Massachusetts, have invented certain Improvements in Electro-Magnetic Printing-Telegraphs, of which the following is a full, clear, and exact description, reference being had to the accompanying drawings making part of this specification, in which—

Figure 1 is a perspective view of my improved instrument; Figs. 2 and 3, details; Figs. 4 and 5, diagrams to be referred to.

This invention has for its object to produce a simple, reliable, and inexpensive printing-telegraph, which will require no attendant at the receiving-station; and consists in the employment of two electro-magnets placed within the same circuit—one for rotating the type-wheel, the other for actuating the printing-hammer—in combination with a polarized relay, which forms an automatic switch that will instantly detect the direction of the current, and cause it, when traveling in one direction, to pass only through the electro-magnet of the type-wheel, and, when reversed so as to travel in the contrary direction, to pass only through the electro-magnet of the printing-hammer, which may thus be brought into operation, to produce the required impression upon the paper, by simply reversing the current at the proper time, no local battery being required at the receiving-station, as all the mechanism is operated by the current from the battery at the transmitting-station.

To enable others skilled in the art to understand and use my invention, I will proceed to describe the manner in which I have carried it out.

In the said drawings, A represents the framework of the instrument, to which is secured the electro-magnet B, which operates the type-wheel C, the periphery of which is provided with the required letters and characters. The armature *b* of the magnet B is attached to a lever, *c*, which is pivoted at *d*, and is bifurcated at its lower end, as seen in Figs. 1 and 2, the two arms *e f* carrying pawls *g h*, which engage with a ratchet-wheel, *i*, on the hollow shaft of the type-wheel C, which revolves on a stud, *k*, projecting from the frame-work.

It will be seen that the pawls *g* and *h* engage with the ratchet-wheel *i* on opposite sides, so that each vibration of the lever *c* backward or forward will rotate the type-wheel, which receives its supply of ink from the roll D, in a well-known manner.

E is the electro-magnet of the printing-hammer, which latter consists of a roll, *i*, secured to the outer end of a lever, G, which is pivoted at *j*, and carries the armature H of the magnet E. The strip of paper upon which the message is to be printed is led from a reel (not shown) over the roll *i*, upon which it is held with a sufficient degree of friction by a spring-arm, *l*, provided with an open slot, *m*, so as to allow the paper to be brought into contact with the edge of the type-wheel when the lever G is raised against the resistance of the spring 6 by the action of the electro-magnet E. The strip of paper is fed forward between the roll *i* and spring-arm *l* after each impression is made, so as to produce the required space between the letters, by means of a pawl, *n*, which, when the lever G descends, engages with a ratchet-wheel, *o*, Fig. 3, secured to the roll *i*, which is thus rotated at the required times, its edges 7 being roughened, so as to prevent the paper from slipping thereon.

The course of the current through the instrument, and the manner in which the latter is operated, will now be described, reference being had particularly to Figs. 1, 4, and 5.

I K are two batteries, so arranged that but one only is employed at a time.

Referring to Fig. 4, when the battery I is in use, the current passes (as indicated by black lines and arrows) from its copper pole *p*, by the wire *q*, to the key *r*; thence, by the wire *s*, to the electro-magnet of a polarized relay, L, which forms an automatic switch, by means of which the course of the current may be changed, as will be hereafter particularly described, it being well known that the passage of a current of electricity in one direction through the electro-magnet of a polarized relay will cause its tongue or lever *u* to be attracted to the pole N, and thereby brought into contact with the pin, *v*, while the reversal of the current will cause it to be attracted to the pole N', and brought into contact with the pin *w*, thereby opening different paths for the current, so that it may be made to pass through either one of the electro-magnets B or E, one of these magnets being excluded or cut out from the circuit while the current is passing through the other. The construction of this polarized relay, however, being well known, and forming no part of my invention, will not be further described.

The instant the current passes from the wire s through the polarized relay the tongue u will be attracted by the pole N and brought into contact with the pin r, when the current will pass by the wire x to the point S, but as the contact is broken at w it cannot follow the wire a', and consequently passes through the electro-magnet B, leaving it by the wire c', and, instead of following this wire to the electro-magnet E, it takes a shorter course, viz., by the wire d' to the tongue u, thence through the contact-pin r to the wire e', and thence to the ground and back to the wire f', (also in connection with the ground,) whence it passes to the zinc pole of the battery I, thereby completing the circuit.

The circuit, after being completed as above described, may be alternately broken and closed by means of an ordinary transmitter, (not shown,) for the purpose of operating the armature b, and thereby rotating the type-wheel C, the mechanism connected with which is so arranged that the circuit requires to be closed and broken once in order to move the wheel C a distance equal to that between two successive letters or characters. This insures the circuit being open whenever a letter is brought into the position to allow of its impression being taken off upon the strip of paper.

When the type-wheel has been rotated (by operating the transmitter) until the desired letter has been brought into position beneath the roll i, the current is reversed by shifting the key r into the position seen in Fig. 5, which disconnects the battery I, and causes the current from the copper pole g' of the battery K to pass, by the wires h' and f', to the ground plate, thence to the distant ground-plate, entering the instrument by the wire e'. This reversal of the current causes the tongue u of the polarized relay to be instantly attracted to the pole N' and brought into contact with the pin w, breaking the contact at r, as seen in Fig. 5.

The action of the polarized relay is so much quicker than that of an ordinary electro-magnet that the lever u is shifted from the point v to the point w before the electro-magnet B has time to act, and this magnet being cut out of the circuit as soon as the tongue u comes in contact with the pin w, the current will pass,

as indicated by the red lines and arrows, Fig. 5, by the wires h' f' e' i', to the electro-magnet E of the printing-hammer, and thence, (instead of passing through the electro-magnet B,) by the shortest course, through the wires c' d', to the tongue u, thence, by the contact-pin w and wires a' x, to the electro-magnet of the polarized relay, and, by the wire s, key r, and wire k', to the zinc pole of the battery K, completing the circuit and causing the armature H to be attracted to the magnet E, raising the lever G and bringing the paper into contact with the letter on the type-wheel, as required. The key r is then moved back into the position seen in Figs. 3 and 4, which again reverses the current and causes it to take the course first described, through the electro-magnet B of the type-wheel, but not through the electro-magnet E, the armature of which ceases to be attracted when the lever G, with the roll i, is drawn down by the spring 6 and the paper fed forward to receive the next impression, as required, when the operation continues as before.

It will thus be seen that by the employment of a polarized relay, as above described, either one of the electro-magnets B or E may be brought into action and the other cut out of the circuit at pleasure by the reversal of the current, which enables me to greatly simplify the construction of printing-telegraphs and reduce their cost.

The above-described invention is designed particularly for transmitting intelligence from a central station to a number of receiving stations included in the circuit, in which case no batteries or operators will be required at the receiving stations; but if messages are to be sent from each station, as well as received, then each instrument will require to be provided with a transmitting instrument, a battery, and an ordinary switch connected with a ground-wire.

What I claim as my invention, and desire to secure by Letters Patent, is—

The two electro-magnets B E, placed within the same circuit, one for operating the type-wheel, the other for operating the printing-hammer, in combination with a polarized relay which forms an automatic switch, whereby either one of the electro-magnets may be brought into action, and the other cut out of the circuit by the reversal of the current, substantially as and for the purpose described.

THOMAS A. EDISON.

Witnesses:
  P. E. TESCHEMACHER,
  W. J. CAMBRIDGE.

Pages 73–75: You might think the electric or hybrid car is a modern invention. Thomas Edison was working on it in 1902.

T. A. EDISON.
ELECTRICAL AUTOMOBILE.
APPLICATION FILED JAN. 9, 1903.

NO MODEL.

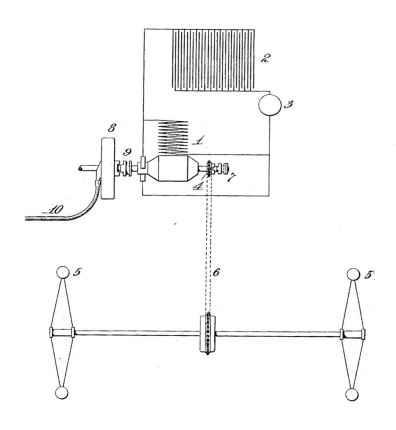

Witnesses:

Jas. F. Coleman

Jno. Rob't Taylor

Inventor

Thomas A. Edison

By Dyer Edmonds & Dyer

Attorneys

UNITED STATES PATENT OFFICE.

THOMAS A. EDISON, OF ORANGE, NEW JERSEY.

ELECTRICAL AUTOMOBILE.

SPECIFICATION forming part of Letters Patent No. 750,102, dated January 19, 1904.

Application filed January 9, 1903. Serial No. 138,427. (No model.)

To all whom it may concern:

Be it known that I, THOMAS A. EDISON, a citizen of the United States, residing at Llewellyn Park, Orange, in the county of Essex and State
5 of New Jersey, have invented a certain new and useful Improvement in Electrical Automobiles, of which the following is a specification.

My invention relates to various new and useful improvements in electric automobiles pro-
10 pelled by storage batteries; and my object is to provide an electric automobile in which the driving-motor may be conveniently and effectively utilized for the purpose of charging the batteries.
15 To this end the invention consists in providing a small steam or other elastic pressure engine, preferably of the turbine type, either connected at all times to the armature of the electric motor or adapted to be connected
20 thereto through a suitable clutch, so that by reversing the electrical connections or by reversing the rotation of the motor-armature the electric motor will be converted into a generator for charging the batteries. A clutch
25 connection can also be effectively utilized for disconnecting the electric motor from the driving-wheels during the charging operation, although it will be of course understood that the driving-wheels may be jacked up, so as
30 to be driven during the charging operation.

In the drawing I illustrate a diagrammatic view of a convenient apparatus for the purpose.

The electric motor 1 is illustrated diagram-
35 matically as being shunt-wound, although, of course, any other winding may be utilized.

2 represents the storage batteries, and 3 a suitable controller either for interposing resistance in the motor-circuit or for effecting
40 variations in the electrical connection between the batteries and the motor for controlling the speed of the latter. On the armature-shaft of the motor is mounted a sprocket-wheel 4, which drives the vehicle-wheels 5 through a chain 6.
45 A clutch 7 may be used for connecting or disconnecting the sprocket-wheel 4 to the armature-shaft.

8 represents a small steam or other fluid pressure engine, preferably of the turbine
50 type, adapted to be connected to or discon-

nected from the motor-armature by a clutch 9. A turbine-engine is preferable on account of its extreme simplicity and lightness. A connection with the engine 8 is made through a hose-section 10 with any suitable source of 55 steam or other fluid pressure.

While I prefer to employ means for connecting and disconnecting the driving element of the engine 8 with the motor 1, it will be understood that the clutch may be dispensed with, 60 and particularly if a turbine-engine is used, whereby its rotating part acts as an effective fly-wheel.

In operation the motor 1 drives the carriage in the usual way, its speed being regulated by 65 the controller 3. When the batteries become depleted, the clutch 7 may be operated to disconnect the sprocket-wheel 4 from the armature-shaft. The clutch 9, if used, connects the engine with the armature-shaft, and the sup- 70 ply-hose 10 is led to the boiler or other source of steam-supply. By now operating the engine 8 to reverse the rotation of the armature-shaft the motor 1 will be converted into a generator to recharge the batteries 2. By means 75 of my present invention the radius of action of electric automobiles is very greatly increased, since even in small towns it is possible to secure a supply of steam where the electric current is not used. When the engine 8 is of the 80 turbine type, it adds but little weight and bulk to the entire apparatus.

Having now described my invention, what I claim as new, and desire to secure by Letters Patent, is as follows: 85

1. In an electric automobile, the combination with the driving-motor and the storage batteries, of a separate fluid-pressure engine connected with the armature-shaft of the motor for operating the latter as a generator for 90 recharging the batteries, and a flexible connection with said engine for supplying fluidpressure thereto, substantially as and for the purposes set forth.

2. In an electric automobile, the combina- 95 tion with the driving-motor and the storage batteries, of a separate rotary fluid-pressure engine connected with the armature-shaft of the motor for operating the latter as a generator for recharging the batteries, and a flexi- 100

ble connection with said engine for supplying fluid-pressure thereto, substantially as and for the purposes set forth.

3. In an electric automobile, the combina-
5 tion with the driving-motor and the storage batteries, of a separate turbine fluid-pressure engine connected with the armature-shaft of the motor for operating the latter as a gener-
10 ator for recharging the batteries, and a flexi-ble connection with said engine for supplying fluid-pressure thereto, substantially as and for the purposes set forth.

4. In an electric automobile, the combina-
15 tion with the operating-motor and batteries, of a fluid-pressure engine normally disconnected from the armature-shaft of the motor but adapted to be connected therewith for operat-ing the motor as a generator for recharging
20 the batteries, and a flexible connection with said engine for supplying fluid-pressure there-to, substantially as and for the purposes set forth.

5. In an electric automobile, the combina-
25 tion with the operating-motor and batteries, of a rotary fluid-pressure engine normally discon-nected from the armature-shaft of the motor but adapted to be connected therewith for op-erating the motor as a generator for recharg-
30 ing the batteries, and a flexible connection with said engine for supplying fluid-pressure thereto, substantially as and for the purposes set forth.

6. In an electric automobile, the combina-tion with the operating-motor and batteries, of a fluid-pressure turbine-engine normally dis-35 connected from the armature-shaft of the mo-tor but adapted to be connected therewith for operating the motor as a generator for re-charging the batteries, and a flexible connec-tion with said engine for supplying the fluid-40 pressure thereto, substantially as and for the purposes set forth.

7. In an electric automobile, the combina-tion with the motor, batteries and connections between the motor and the driving-wheels, of 45 a fluid-pressure engine connected to the arma-ture-shaft for operating the motor as a gen-erator, and means for disconnecting the arma-ture-shaft from the driving-wheels, and a flexi-ble connection with said engine for supplying 50 fluid-pressure thereto, substantially as and for the purposes set forth.

8. In an electric automobile, the combina-tion with the driving-motor, batteries and con-nections between the motor and driving-55 wheels, of a fluid-pressure engine normally dis-connected from the armature-shaft but adapt-ed to be connected therewith to operate the motor as a generator, and a flexible connec-tion with said engine for supplying the fluid-60 pressure thereto, substantially as and for the purposes set forth.

This specification signed and witnessed this 18th day of December, 1902.

THOMAS A. EDISON.

Witnesses:
FRANK L. DYER,
JNO. ROBT. TAYLOR.

Pages 76–84: Take a look at these two patents for an expandable pulley, designed to allow the user to change the gear ratio on the fly. The first patent uses strings; the second, nine years later, is a much more developed idea.

T. A. EDISON.
EXPANSIBLE PULLEY.

No. 476,984.

Patented June 14, 1892.

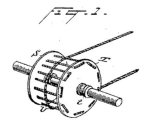

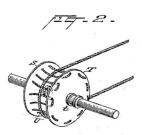

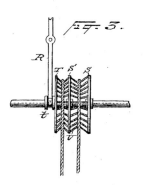

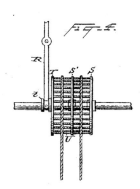

Witnesses

Norris A. Clark

W. Pelzer

Inventor

Thomas A. Edison

By his Attorneys

UNITED STATES PATENT OFFICE.

THOMAS A. EDISON, OF LLEWELLYN PARK, NEW JERSEY.

EXPANSIBLE PULLEY.

SPECIFICATION forming part of Letters Patent No. 476,984, dated June 14, 1892.

Original application filed June 10, 1890, Serial No. 354,946. Divided and this application filed August 28, 1890. Serial No. 363,255. (No model.)

To all whom it may concern:

Be it known that I, THOMAS A. EDISON, a citizen of the United States, residing a Llewellyn Park, in the county of Essex and State of New Jersey, have invented a certain new and useful Improvement in Expansible Pulleys, (Case No. 872,) of which the following is a specification.

This invention relates to power-transmitting pulleys, and the main objects are to provide a simple and efficient pulley the working circumference of which may be varied as required; and the invention consists in the several features and combinations hereinafter described and claimed.

In the accompanying drawings, forming a part hereof, Figures 1 and 2 are perspective views of a simple form of my expansible pulley, and Figs. 3 and 4 are elevations of a compound expanding pulley constructed upon the same principle.

S is a disk fixed against sliding movement, and T is a sliding disk adapted to be moved by the arm R. These disks are provided near their periphery with smooth holes, through which is threaded a rope U the ends of which are suitably fastened. As the sliding disk T is moved toward the fixed disk S the strain of the endless belt will take up the slack in the pulley-rope U and cause the pulley to act as if of a definitely-smaller size, as shown in Fig. 2. If a pulley adapted to carry two ropes or belts is required, the same construction can be employed, as shown in Figs. 3 and 4, in which an additional fixed disk S' is used, placed between the disks S and T and having holes through which the rope U passes. As the sliding disk T is moved toward the middle fixed disk S' the pulley-rope will be drawn through the holes in this disk S' by the strain of the driving-belt and the contracted pulley will appear as in Fig. 4. It is evident that the same result could be obtained by other relative movements of the disks such as by rotating the disk T instead of sliding it. The sliding disk T in both the simple and com-

pound pulley is provided with a grooved collar *t*, by means of which this disk can be moved, as will be readily understood.

I am aware that the heads of expansible pulleys have been joined together by loose or jointed rods; but my invention is confined to the use of connections of flexible material, such as rope. This furnishes a cheap device and one whose construction and operation are exceedingly simple and which is not likely to get out of order. By the phrase "one of which (disks) is movable relative to the other" it is not intended to convey the idea that the second disk must necessarily be stationary, but the movement must be such as to change the relative location of the disks. The terms "ropes" and "cords" obviously include other flexible strands or bodies which can be used in the manner above described, such as leather straps, chains, &c., (as distinguished from rigid rods or other rigid bodies.)

This application is a division required by the Patent Office of a prior application filed June 10, 1890, on which a patent has been issued, No. 436,970, dated September 23, 1890.

What I claim is—

1. An expansible pulley having heads or disks, one of which is movable relative to the other, and a rope connection between the disks, upon which the belt travels and the working circumference of which is made smaller or larger, as desired, substantially as set forth.

2. An expansible pulley having heads or disks, one of which is movable relative to the other, and a connection between the same by means of flexible ropes or cords threaded through holes in the disks, substantially as set forth.

This specification signed and witnessed this 9th day of August, 1890.

THOS. A. EDISON.

Witnesses:
  RICHD. N. DYER,
  W. PELZER.

No. 641,281.

Patented Jan. 16, 1900.

T. A. EDISON & C. M. JOHNSON.

EXPANDING PULLEY.

(Application filed Apr. 24, 1899.)

(No Model.)

3 Sheets—Sheet 1.

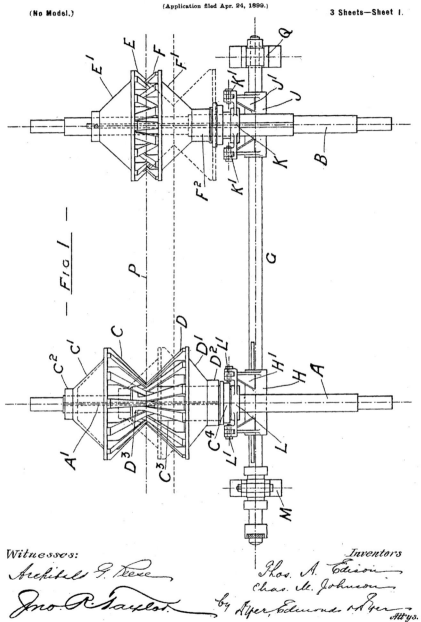

Fig 1

Witnesses:

Archibald G. Reese

Jno. R. Taylor

Inventors

Thos. A. Edison
Chas. M. Johnson

by Dyer, Edmonds & Dyer,
Attys.

No. 641,281.

Patented Jan. 16, 1900.

T. A. EDISON & C. M. JOHNSON.

EXPANDING PULLEY.

(Application filed Apr. 24, 1899.)

(No Model.)

3 Sheets—Sheet 2.

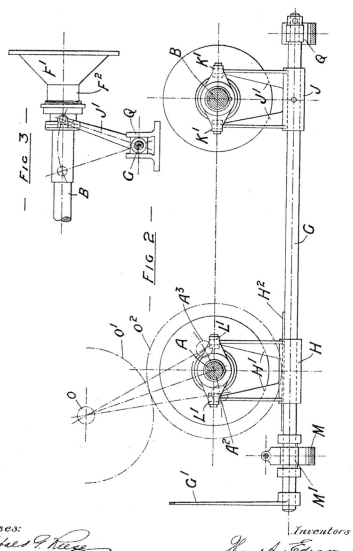

Witnesses:
Archibald P. Reeve
Jno. R. Taylor

Inventors
Thos. A. Edison
Chas. M. Johnson
By Dyer, Edmonds & Dyer Attys.

SimplyCharlotteMason.com

79

No. 641,281.

Patented Jan. 16, 1900.

T. A. EDISON & C. M. JOHNSON.

EXPANDING PULLEY.

(Application filed Apr. 24, 1899.)

(No Model.)

3 Sheets—Sheet 3.

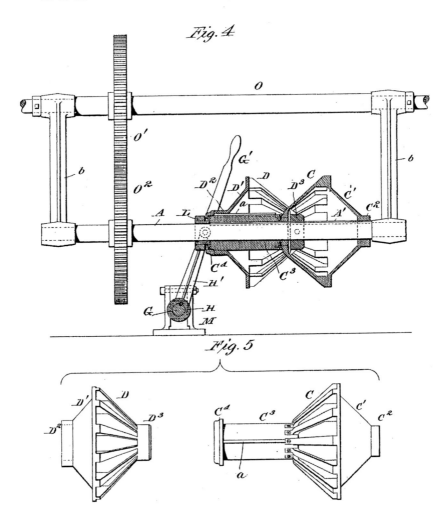

Fig. 4.

Fig. 5.

Witnesses:
Jas. F. Coleman
Jno. R. Taylor

Inventors
Thomas A. Edison
Charles M. Johnson
by Dyer, Edmonds & Dyer
Att'ys.

UNITED STATES PATENT OFFICE.

THOMAS A. EDISON, OF LLEWELLYN PARK, NEW JERSEY, AND CHARLES M. JOHNSON, OF REDHILL, ENGLAND.

EXPANDING PULLEY.

SPECIFICATION forming part of Letters Patent No. 641,281, dated January 16, 1900.

Application filed April 24, 1899. Serial No. 714,340. (No model.)

To all whom it may concern:

Be it known that we, THOMAS A. EDISON, residing at Llewellyn Park, in the county of Essex and State of New Jersey, and CHARLES
5 M. JOHNSON, residing at Redhill, in the county of Surrey, England, citizens of the United States, have invented certain new and useful Improvements in Expanding Pulleys, of which the following is a specification.
10 Our invention relates to various new and useful improvements in expanding pulleys adapted to convert a uniform velocity of a driving-shaft into varying velocities of a driven belt or to convert the uniform velocity
15 of a driving-belt into varying velocities of a driven shaft.

The object of the invention is to provide an improved construction of expansible pulley which will be possessed of great rigidity and
20 wherein the working diameter may be quickly and easily varied.

The invention preferably comprises two of the improved expansible pulleys arranged on parallel shafts and connected by a belt, where-
25 by power will be transmitted from one shaft to the other. When two expansible pulleys are employed, the invention comprises devices for simultaneously varying their working diameters in inverse directions, whereby the
30 relative speeds of rotation of the shafts will be changed. If a crossed belt is employed, when two expansible pulleys are used, with devices for simultaneously operating them, the belt will be maintained uniformly tight
35 irrespective of the changes in the diameter of the two pulleys, since the increase in diameter of one will exactly compensate for the decrease in the diameter of the other.

The invention also comprises means for
40 tightening the belt when necessary and for keeping it in a tight condition.

In carrying out our invention we employ an expansible pulley comprising, essentially, two intercalated cones movable toward and away
45 from each other and each consisting of a series of ribs or bars which are connected at their outer or enlarged ends to tapering sheaths, into which work the bars or ribs of the companion cone, and means being pro-
50 vided to shift the cones relatively. When the invention comprises a pair of these ex-

pansible pulleys arranged on parallel shafts, one conical section of each pulley will be stationary with respect to the shaft, the other
55 being movable longitudinally thereon, but rotating therewith. We employ a rock-shaft extending at right angles to the driving and driven shafts and carrying arms which are connected with the movable conical section
60 of each expansible pulley. The movable section of one expansible pulley is arranged with respect to the corresponding section of the other so that when movement of both
65 takes place in one direction by the operation of the rock-shaft the working diameter of one pulley will be increased, while the working diameter of the other will be decreased. Not only will this provide for changes in the speed of the belt, but in effecting a speed
70 change the belt will be shifted always parallel to the plane of its driving movement, whereby if a crossed belt is used it will always be maintained tight.

When the invention comprises additional
75 means for tightening the belt, we hang the rock-shaft from the driving and driven shafts and support one of the latter by a pair of links depending from a power-shaft or work-shaft, whereby the former may move radially
80 with respect to the other. Power is communicated between these two shafts by suitable gearing which is unaffected by the radial movements—as, for example, by two engaging gears. In this way the two shafts carrying
85 the expansible pulleys may be moved laterally with respect to each other to secure the proper tension of the belt without affecting the transmission of power either to or from the expansible pulleys or to or from each
90 other.

In order that our invention may be better understood, attention is directed to the accompanying drawings, forming a part of this specification, and in which—
95 Figure 1 is a plan of an apparatus illustrating an embodiment of our invention, showing two shafts carrying the two conical pulleys with means for simultaneously adjusting them and showing in dotted and full lines
100 the extreme position of the conical sections. In this view the chain-line illustrates the position of the belt when the expansible pul-

leys are in the position shown in full lines, while the dotted line illustrates the position of the belt when the sections of the expansible pulleys are in the position shown in dotted lines. Fig. 2 is a side elevation illustrating a power or work shaft and showing the preferred means for effecting the adjustment of the belt; Fig. 3, a section on the line 3 3 of Fig. 2, showing only a portion of one of the expansible pulleys; Fig. 4, a longitudinal section through the shaft A of Figs. 1 and 2, and Fig. 5 a plan view showing the conical sections C and D relatively separated.

In all of the above views corresponding parts are represented by the same letters of reference.

A and B represent the two shafts, the former being the driving-shaft and the latter the driven shaft. Each shaft carries an expanding pulley formed of two opposed conical members C D and E F. In the embodiment of the invention illustrated in the drawings each conical member is formed of a number of bars or ribs which constitute the conical surface, the bars of one member being intercalated between those of the other member of the pulley, the points of intersection forming, substantially, a V-groove, at the bottom of which the belt or band engages. The cones are carried upon their respective shafts in such a manner that one member of each pair is fixed thereupon and the other member capable of adjustment by axial movement upon the shaft. The members C and F in the present case are adjustable, and the members D and E are stationary. The axial adjustment of the conical members C and F is in the example illustrated effected simultaneously by connections operated from a rock-shaft G in such a manner that the belt travels axially parallel to itself and remains uniformly tight for all the attainable velocity ratios of the shafts A and B, as will be presently explained.

Regarding the preferred constructional details of the expansible pulleys, each set of the ribs or bars C, D, E, and F is supported at its larger circumference by a conical sheath C′, D′, E′, and F′, respectively. The sheaths of each conical member will, when the pulley is expanded, receive and cover the inner extremities of the companion members, as will be obvious. The inner extremities of the bars or ribs C unite to form or are secured to a sleeve C³, and the inner end of the sheath C′ is supported by a boss C², both the boss C² and sleeve C³ being free to move axially upon the shaft A, but either or both being rotatively driven from the shaft in any suitable way, as from a feather A′. The sleeve C³ terminates at C⁴ in a collar, the purpose of which will be explained. The inner ends of the bars or ribs D of the other conical member unite to form a boss D³, which is keyed or otherwise fixed to the shaft A, and the other ends are secured to the sheath D′, whose smaller diameter forms or is connected to the collar D². The sleeve C³ works within the collar D²,

but may be driven therefrom, if desired, by a key or feather a, as shown in Figs. 4 and 5. The bars C are thus driven from the shaft at the boss C² and at the sleeve C³ through the feather A′, and the bars D are driven through the boss D³, either alone or in connection with a driving connection from the sleeve C³ at the collar D².

The pulley carried by the shaft B is similar in construction to that on the shaft A, except that the bars E being fixed and the bars F adjustable axially the inner ends of the former terminate in a boss (not shown) fixed to the shaft instead of in a movable sleeve, while the sleeve F² at the small end of the sheath F′ is capable of axial movement, as is also a sleeve (not shown) in which the inner ends of the bars F terminate.

The adjusting device for shifting the movable sections of each expansible pulley with respect to the stationary sections thereof comprises a rock-shaft G, operated by a hand-lever G′ and carrying a sleeve H, splined to the shaft on a feather H², and a second sleeve J, fixed to said shaft. Each of these sleeves carries a pair of arms H′ H′ and J′ J′, respectively. The arms H′ are pivoted to projections L′ on a sleeve L, arranged to slide upon the shaft A, the latter rotating freely within it. The sleeve L engages the end of the collar C⁴, so as to impart axial movement thereto without interfering with the rotation thereof. If desired, an antifriction-bearing may be interposed between the collar and sleeve. A similar connection is provided by a sleeve K, having projections K′, within which the arms J′ are pivoted, the said sleeve K engaging with and moving the sleeve F² of the movable member of the expansible pulley on the shaft B. The rock-shaft G will be thus supported from the shafts A and B through the links H′ and J′. It is guided at its ends in bearings M and Q, as shown more particularly in Fig. 3, whereby a slight rise and fall of the shaft will be permitted. The bearing-box for the rock-shaft G, working in the bearing M, is shown at M′, Fig. 2. The shaft A in this instance is suspended by links b b, as shown in Fig. 4, from a power or work shaft O, from which it is driven or which it itself drives, preferably, by toothed gearing O′ O², as shown. By suspending the shaft A from the power or work shaft O by means of links b b, as explained, the shaft A may be swung relatively to tighten or loosen the belt, the extreme positions of the shaft being indicated in Fig. 2 by the reference-letters A² and A³.

The operation will be as follows: The position shown in full lines in Fig. 1 illustrates the pulley C D at its smallest diameter and E F at its largest diameter. If it is now desired to increase the velocity of the shaft B relatively to that of A, assuming that the latter is driven from the former, the lever G′ is moved so as to cause the cone member C to approach the member D and the cone member F to recede from the member E. The extreme extent of this movement in this direction is shown in dotted lines in Fig. 1. The effect produced on the belt is to cause it to travel axially with the movable cones and parallel to its own plane of rotation, and if it is a crossed belt it will remain uniformly tight at all velocity ratios of A and B, since the increase of the working diameter at one of the expansible pulleys is compensated by a decrease in the working diameter at the other pulley. If it is desired to adjust the tightness of the belt, this may be effected by moving the shaft A about the center of the shaft O, causing the shafts A and B to separate. In this movement the sleeve H will slide axially on the shaft G, while the inclination of the latter will be slightly changed, the end bearings thereof working in the guides M and Q.

Having now described our invention, what we claim as new, and desire to secure by Letters Patent, is as follows:

1. In an expansible pulley, the combination of a conical section fixed against lateral movement, a conical section movable laterally, said conical sections comprising intercalated bars or ribs, a conical sheath for the movable section inverted with respect to the same, and a sleeve to which the inner ends of the movable section are secured, substantially as set forth.

2. In an expansible pulley, the combination of a conical section fixed against lateral movement, a conical section movable laterally, said conical sections comprising intercalated bars or ribs, a conical sheath for the movable section inverted with respect to the same, a sleeve to which the inner ends of the movable section are secured, and means for moving said sleeve to vary the working diameter of the pulley, substantially as set forth.

3. The combination of two expansible pulleys, each comprising two intercalated conical sections, one section of each set being stationary, the stationary element of one set being reverse to that of the other set, whereby when the movable sections of both sets are moved longitudinally in one direction or the other the line of the working diameter of both pulleys will be shifted in parallelism, substantially as set forth.

4. The combination of two expansible pulleys, each comprising two intercalated conical sections, one section of each set being stationary, the stationary element of one set being reverse to that of the other set, whereby when the movable sections of both sets are moved longitudinally in one direction or the other the line of the working diameter of both pulleys will be shifted in parallelism, and means for simultaneously shifting the movable section of each pulley, substantially as set forth.

5. The combination of two expansible pulleys, each comprising two intercalated conical sections, one section of each set being stationary, the stationary element of one set

being reverse to that of the other set, whereby when the movable sections of both sets are moved longitudinally in one direction or the other the line of the working diameter of both pulleys will be shifted in parallelism, a rock-shaft and connections between said rock-shaft and the movable sections of both pulleys, whereby the latter may be shifted simultaneously, substantially as set forth.

6. The combination of two expansible pulleys, each comprising two intercalated conical sections, one section of each set being stationary, the stationary element of one set being reverse to that of the other set, whereby when the movable sections of both sets are moved longitudinally in one direction or the other the line of the working diameter of both pulleys will be shifted in parallelism, and means for moving the pulleys toward and away from each other for adjusting the tension of a belt between them, substantially as set forth.

7. The combination of two expansible pulleys, each comprising two intercalated conical sections, one section of each set being stationary, the stationary element of one set being reverse to that of the other set, whereby when the movable sections of both sets are moved longitudinally in one direction or the other the line of the working diameter of both pulleys will be shifted in parallelism, a rock-shaft, connections between the rock-shaft and the movable section of each pulley for shifting the same, and means for moving one pulley laterally with respect to the rock-shaft, whereby the tension of a belt may be varied, substantially as set forth.

8. The combination of two expansible pulleys, each comprising two intercalated conical sections, one section of each set being stationary, the stationary element of one set being reverse to that of the other set, whereby when the movable sections of both sets are moved longitudinally in one direction or the other the line of the working diameter of both pulleys will be shifted in parallelism, and a rock-shaft having arms which are attached to the movable section of each pulley and from which the rock-shaft will be supported, substantially as set forth.

9. The combination of two expansible pulleys, each comprising two intercalated conical sections, one section of each set being stationary, the stationary element of one set being reverse to that of the other set, whereby when the movable sections of both sets are moved longitudinally in one direction or the other the line of the working diameter of both pulleys will be shifted in parallelism, a rock-shaft having arms which are attached to the movable section of each pulley and from which the rock-shaft will be supported, and end bearings for said rock-shaft permitting vertical movements thereof, substantially as set forth.

10. The combination of two expansible pulleys, each comprising two intercalated con-

ical sections, one section of each set being stationary, the stationary element of one set being reverse to that of the other set, whereby when the movable sections of both sets are moved longitudinally in one direction or the other the line of the working diameter of both pulleys will be shifted in parallelism, a rock-shaft having arms which are attached to the movable section of each pulley and from which the rock-shaft will be supported, end bearings for said rock-shaft permitting vertical movements thereof, and means for shifting one of the pulleys toward and away from the other to adjust the tension of a belt, causing the ends of the rock-shaft to be moved in the bearings therefor, substantially as set forth.

11. The combination of two expansible pulleys, each comprising two intercalated conical sections, one section of each set being stationary, the stationary element of one set being reverse to that of the other set, whereby when the movable sections of both sets are moved longitudinally in one direction or the other the line of the working diameter of both pulleys will be shifted in parallelism, a rock-shaft having arms which are attached to the movable section of each pulley and from which the rock-shaft will be supported, end bearings for said rock-shaft permitting vertical movements thereof, means for shifting one of the pulleys toward and away from the other to adjust the tension of a belt, causing the ends of the rock-shaft to be moved in the bearings therefor, and a power or work shaft with respect to which the adjustable pulley is radially movable, substantially as set forth.

This specification signed and witnessed this 10th day of April, 1899.

THOS. A. EDISON.

This specification signed and witnessed this 28th day of March, 1899.

CHARLES M. JOHNSON.

Witnesses to signature of Thomas A. Edison:

    J. F. RANDOLPH,
    ARCHIBALD G. REESE.

Witnesses to signature of Charles M. Johnson:

    THOMAS JEFFREY,
    JAMES ALEXANDER.

Pages 86–89: Not all of Edison's ideas were successful. Here is his patent for a flying machine, filed five years after the Wright brothers' first flight. How would you like to fly on a machine that was composed of box kites attached with piano wire and spinning in a circle?

T. A. EDISON.
FLYING MACHINE.
APPLICATION FILED NOV. 16, 1908.

970,616.

Patented Sept. 20, 1910.
2 SHEETS—SHEET 1.

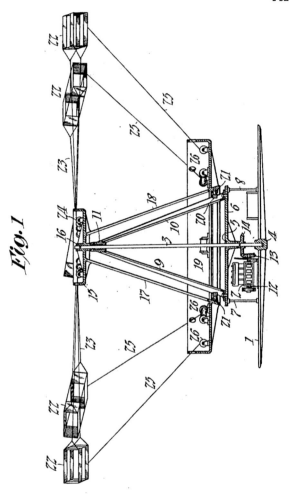

Fig. 1

Witnesses:
Frank D. Lewis
Dyer Smith

Inventor:
Thomas A. Edison
by Frank L. Dyer
Atty.

T. A. EDISON.

FLYING MACHINE.

APPLICATION FILED NOV. 16, 1908.

970,616.

Patented Sept. 20, 1910.

2 SHEETS—SHEET 2.

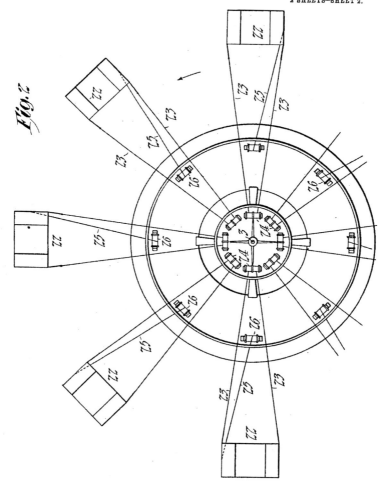

Fig. 2

Witnesses:

Frank D. Lewis

Dyer Smith

Inventor:

Thomas A. Edison

By Frank L. Dyer

Atty.

UNITED STATES PATENT OFFICE.

THOMAS A. EDISON, OF LLEWELLYN PARK, ORANGE, NEW JERSEY.

FLYING-MACHINE.

970,616. Specification of Letters Patent. **Patented Sept. 20, 1910.**

Application filed November 16, 1908. Serial No. 462,895.

To all whom it may concern:

Be it known that I, THOMAS ALVA EDISON, a citizen of the United States, and residing at Llewellyn Park, Orange, county of Es-
5 sex, and State of New Jersey, have invented certain new and useful Improvements in Flying-Machines, of which the following is a full, clear, and concise description.

This invention relates to means for lifting
10 a heavier-than-air flying machine from the ground and to maintain it at any desired distance from the ground, and has for its object the provision of a series of aeroplane members, which, on being rotated through the
15 air about a central axis of the machine as a center, and held at a given angle to the horizontal, will exert a lifting force due to the pressure of the atmosphere upon them as they are rotated therethrough, which lifting
20 force is transmitted to the body of the machine. Preferably, these aeroplane members are in the form of box kites which are connected to the frame of the machine by flexible means as cords or wires, and are
25 sustained during rotation by centrifugal force. Means are provided by which the inclination from front to back of the aeroplane members may be changed, the lifting force exerted by the air
30 on such members depending on the angle of inclination of said members as well as on the speed of rotation.

My invention also comprises the combinations and details of construction described in
35 the following specification and claims.

The preferred form of my invention is shown in the accompanying drawings, forming part of this specification, in which—

Figure 1 is a side elevation, partly in sec-
40 tion, and Fig. 2 is a plan view of the same.

The machine carries a floor or basket 1, designed to carry passengers, machinery, etc. A gasolene engine or other prime mover 2, as illustrated diagrammatically, is carried
45 by this floor, and means for propulsion, such as propellers, and likewise, steering apparatus, etc., not shown, but well-known to the art, may be carried. The apparatus is provided with a central vertical shaft 3, which
50 rotates in a bearing 4 in the floor or staging 1. The shaft 3 is likewise supported by a bearing 5 in horizontal member 6, which is supported from floor 1 as by vertical members 7 and 8. Members 9, 10, etc., mounted
55 on the member 6 support a sleeve 11 which

constitutes the upper bearing for vertical shaft 3.

Shaft 3 is rotated within bearing surfaces 4, 5 and 11 from the engine 2 which carries on the shaft 12 thereof, a bevel gear 60 13 meshing with bevel gear 14, pinned or fastened to shaft 3. Upper and lower members are fastened to shaft 3 to rotate therewith and are likewise fastened together. The upper member 15 is formed with a cen- 65 tral hub or sleeve 16 fastened to shaft 3, which bears on sleeve 11 of the stationary frame of the machine whereon it may revolve with the aid of any anti-friction device. This platform 15 is secured as by 70 members 17, 18 to a lower platform or horizontal member 19, which is adapted to rotate about the stationary frame, bearing in its rotation on member 20 of said frame, which constitutes a ring, rollers 21, 21 of the 75 rotating platform 19 having rolling engagement therewith.

The aeroplane consists, as stated, preferably of box kites 22, which are supported preferably by piano wires or other flexible 80 means 23, which extend from loops attached, one to the forward end, the other to the rear end of the inner side of each of the kites. These wires 23 are secured to rotating platform 15 at the upper end of ro- 85 tating shaft 3, preferably by means of reels 24, by which the length of connections 23 may be regulated. By such connection, when shaft 3 is rotated, the kites 22 are acted on by centrifugal force to rotate in 90 the horizontal plane of reels 24 when the speed of rotation of shaft 3 is sufficiently great. The tendency of the center of gravity of the kites to fly to the greatest possible radial distance from shaft 3 would 95 cause the kites to rotate with the upper and lower members thereof horizontal, the side to which wires 23 are attached being the inner side during such rotation, if no additional means were provided to cause said 100 upper and lower members to assume a fore and aft slant. Piano wires, or other flexible connections 25 constitute such means, however, and are attached to the edges of the kites which constitute the rear edges 105 during rotation, these wires being attached to the lower rotating platform 19 by means of reels 26. By means of these reels a greater or a less amount of wire 25 may be wound in or let out, thus controlling the 110

horizontal angle of members 22 during their rotation. The kites 22, when so governed, constitute practically a screw, the pitch of which may be changed. The lifting force
5 caused by the revolution of members 22 is due to the vertical component of the force exerted by the atmosphere upon the kites in their rotation. This force increases, of course, with the velocity at which the kites
10 travel in their circular path. This force likewise varies with the angle of inclination of the kites as they are forced through the air, and this may be regulated through reels 26. The tendency of the centrifugal force
15 acting on the kites is to keep the forward end of the kites up to the horizontal plane in which reels 24 are situated. Cords 25 restrain the tendency of the rear ends of the kites to also revolve in the same horizontal
20 plane, and by shortening these cords, the angle of inclination of the kites may be increased. If desired, reels 26 may be connected together so that the angle of horizontal inclination of all of the kites may be
25 instantly changed at will by the operator of the machine, this change of the angle of inclination constituting means for governing the lifting force exerted on the machine. If desired, also, spring connections may be
30 provided between reels 26 and wires 25, adjusted for any desired speed of rotation to allow reels 26 to act in tension between certain limits, and to allow the angle of pitch of the kites to vary somewhat from a given
35 desired angle according to the conditions.

It is obvious that kite members 22 may take the form of any aeroplane members now known to the art, either of flat surfaces or surfaces somewhat curved, and further-
40 more, that various changes in the construction and details of the device disclosed may be made without departing from the spirit of my invention.

Having now described my invention, what
45 I claim and desire to secure by Letters Patent is as follows:

1. In a flying machine, the combination with a vertical shaft, a frame affixed thereto, and means for imparting continuous rota-
50 tion to the same, of a series of box kites, flexible means for connecting the same to the frame, and means for regulating the angle at which said kites are rotated by the said shaft, substantially as described.

2. In a flying machine, the combination 55 with a frame and means for rotating the same, of a series of kites, and flexible means for connecting the same to the frame, so arranged that the kites rotate with the frame under the influence of centrifugal 60 force, and at a constant angle to the horizontal, the forward ends being maintained in a plane above that of the rear ends of said kites, substantially as described.

3. In a flying machine, the combination 65 with a frame and means for rotating the same, of a series of kites, and flexible means for connecting the same to the frame, so arranged that the kites rotate with the frame under the influence of centrifugal force, 70 and at a constant angle to the horizontal, the forward ends being maintained in a plane above that of the rear ends of said kites, and means for varying the said angle, substantially as described. 75

4. In a flying machine, the combination of a plane member, adapted to be flown as a kite, a central frame, flexible connections between said frame and one edge of said member, a flexible connection between the 80 rear part of said member and a point on said frame below the point of attachment of the first mentioned connections, and means for rotating said frame, substantially as described. 85

5. In a flying machine, the combination of a series of kite members, a central frame, means for rotating the frame, cords connecting the front and rear of the inner edge of each kite member with the central frame, 90 a cord connecting the rear of each kite member with the frame at a point lower than the point of attachment of the first mentioned cords, and means for adjusting at will the lengths of said cords, substantially 95 as described.

This specification signed and witnessed this 20th day of August 1908.

THOS. A. EDISON.

Witnesses:
FRANK L. DYER,
DYER SMITH.

Pages 90–94: These pages from Edison's diary give us a peek inside his personal thoughts and display his sense of humor. Dot was his first daughter, born in 1873.

very is very busy cleaning the abode of our deaf and dumb parrot—she has fed it tons of edibles, and never got a sound out of it. This bird has the taciturnity of a statue, and the dirt producing capacity of a drove of buffalo.

This is by far the nicest day of this season, neither too hot or too cold.— it blooms on the apex of perfection — an Edenday Good day for an angels pic nic, They could lunch on the smell of flowers and new mown hay, drink the moisture of the air, and dance to the hum of bees,   Fancy the Soul of Plato astride of a butterfly, riding around Menlo Park with a lunch basket   Nature is bound to smile somehow, Holzer has a little dog which just came on the veranda, The face of this dog was a dismal as a bust of Dante, but the dog wagged its tail continuously – This is evidently the way a dog laughs — I wonder if dogs ever go up to flowers and smell them – I think not – flowers were never intended for dogs, and perhaps only incidentally for man, evidently Darwin has it right — They make themselves pretty to attract the insect world who are the transportation agents of their pollen,   pollen freight via B^{ee} Line   There is a bumblebees nest somewhere near this veranda, several times one came near me — some little information (acquired experimentally) I obtained when a

small boy causes me to lose all delight in watching the
navigation of this armed flower burglar.

Had dinner at 3 P.M. ruins of a chicken, rice pudding - I eat
too quick - at 4 oclock Dot came around with her horse
"Colonel" and took me out riding — beautiful roads — saw
10 acre lot full cultivated red raspberries. "a burying ground"
so to speak, — got this execrable pun off on Dot   Dot says
she is going to write a novel already started on — she has
the judgement of a girl of 16 although only 12   We
passed through the town of Metuchen, this town was named
after an Indian chief, they called him Metuchen the chief of the
rolling lands, the country being undulating. Dot laughed
heartily when I told her about a church being a heavenly
fire-escape.   Returned from drive at 5 PM
commenced read short sketches of life: Macauley Sidney
Smith, Dickens & Charlotte Bronte,   Macauley when only
4 years ago omniverous reader, used book language in his
childish conversation, when 5 years old, lady spilled some
hot coffee on his legs. after awhile she asked him if he was
better — he replied — "Madam the agony has abated"
Macauleys mother must have built his mind several years
before his body. Sidney Smiths flashes of wit a perfect —
to call them chestnuts would be literary blasphemy -

They are wandering jewlets to wander forever in the
printers' world— Dont like Dickens— dont know why- I'l
stock my literary cellar with his works later.
Charlotte Bronte was like DeQuincy. what a nice married
couple they would have been I must read Jane Eyre.
— played a little on the piano - its badly out of tune - two
keys have lost their voice,
Dot just read to me outlines of her proposed novel, the
basis seems to be a marriage under duress - I told her
that in case of a marriage to put in bucketfulls of
misery. This would make it realistic, speaking of
realism in painting etc Steele Mackaye at a dinner
given to H H Porter. Wm Winter and myself told us of a
difinition of modern realism given by some frenchman
whose name I have forgotten, " Realism, a dirty
long haired painter sitting on the head of a bust of
Shakespeare painting a pair of old boot boots covered
with dung " The bell rings for supper Igve
Sardines the principal attraction - on seeing them was
attacked by a stroke of vivid memory of some sardines I
eat last winter that caused a rebellion in the labyrinth
of my stomach — could scarcely swallow them today

They nearly did the "return ball" act.   After supper
Dot pitched a ball to me several dozen times - first I ever
tried to catch. It was a hard as Nero's heart - nearly broke
my baby-finger — gave it up — learned Dot and Maggie how
to play "Duck on the rock" They both thought it great fun,
and this is sunday —   My conscience seems to be oblivious
of sunday - it must be incrusted with a sort of irreligious
tartar. If I was not so deaf I might go to church
and get it taken off or at least loosened - eccavi &
will read the new version of the bible
Holzer is going to use the old laboratory for the purpose of
hatching chickens artificially by an electric incubator. He is
very enthusiastic - gave me full details — he is a very patient
and careful experimenter - think he will succeed - everything
succeeded in that old laboratory —   Just think
electricity employed to cheat a poor hen out of the pleasures
of maternity — Machine born chickens — What is home
without a mother   I suggested to H that he
vaccinate his hens with chicken pox virus, then the eggs
would have their embryo heriditarily innoculated + none
of the chickens would have the disease. for economys
sake he could start with one hen and rooster. He being

a scientific man with no farm experience I explained the necessity of having a rooster, he saw the force of this suggestion at once. The sun has left us on time, am going to read from the enclycopedia Brittanica to steady my nerves and go to bed early. I will shut my eyes and imagine a terraced abyss, each terrace occupied by a beautiful maiden to the first I will deliver my mind and they will pass it down down to the uttermost depths of silence and oblivion - Went to bed worked my imagination for a supply of maidens, only saw Mina Dacey & Mamma scheeme busted - sleep.

Woodside Villa
    Boston Harbor